GALAXIES AND COSMOLOGY

the physics and astronomy of

PAUL W. HODGE

Associate Professor of Astronomy

University of Washington

galaxies and cosmology

※
※
※

McGraw-Hill Book Company

New York • St. Louis • San Francisco • Toronto • London • Sydney

McGraw-Hill Series in
UNDERGRADUATE ASTRONOMY
Gerald S. Hawkins, Consulting Editor

BALDWIN: the moon
BRANDT: the sun and stars
HAWKINS: meteors, comets, and meteorites
HODGE: galaxies and cosmology
LUNDQUIST: space science

galaxies and cosmology

Library of Congress Catalog Card Number: 66–16050
1234567890BN7321069876

TO ANN

PREFACE

This book, one of a series on astronomy, is intended to fill a gap of long standing. The lack of a text or any generally comprehensive book on galaxies has made teaching a course on the subject an awkward task for me, and I know that my students have suffered from this lack too. We have had to use, as best we could, the few articles that are available in various compendia and symposium volumes, and these have sometimes led to incomplete or lopsided views of the field of extragalactic astronomy.

To relieve this situation, I have reworked, reorganized, and rewritten my notes for lectures on galaxies given at Harvard and at the University of California at Berkeley. I have attempted to cover all the principal facts and relationships of extragalactic astronomy and to develop, as far as can be done without extensive mathematics, the principal methods of investigation and some important theories. The text is geared to the undergraduate student (or the independent reader), but an early copy of it was used in a graduate course at Berkeley, where important papers in technical journals were assigned to supplement it.

The essentially nonmathematical nature of the presentation allows the book to be used by the nonstudent, as well. Anyone with some knowledge of the basic astronomical terminology can read these pages and learn of some of astronomy's most exciting frontiers. Numerous specific examples are given in detail to aid the reader to form an impression of methods and concepts. An appendix of discussion questions and problems for each chapter is included for class or study use.

Paul W. Hodge

CONTENTS

1 introduction

Currently the two most important goals of the astronomer who specializes in the extragalactic universe are an understanding of the nature of the universe as a whole and a knowledge of the pattern of the evolution of galaxies.

The nature of the universe is the subject of cosmology, a subject that can be approached from the point of view either of observations or of theory. An observational cosmologist pursues his goal by obtaining as clear a notion as his instruments allow of the extent, the scale, and the gross properties of the observable universe. A theoretical cosmologist approaches his problem mathematically by attempting to construct a universe in terms of a physical principle, a geometrical model, or both. The true nature of our universe, when it is discovered, will come from a combination of the results of both kinds of pursuit.

The evolution of galaxies is a very young and complex subject. It is the motivation for many individual projects dealing with specific properties of galaxies, for instance, the determination of the masses, the dynamics, and content of galaxies of various types and at various distances. Certain special problems have arisen, particularly those connected with galaxies that are radio sources and that seem to have experienced in their recent past gigantic explosive events. The relevance of all these problems to that of the evolution of galaxies is the subject of one of the chapters of this text but underlies the subject of all chapters.

PROPERTIES OF GALAXIES

Assembled in Table 1.1 are many of the various recognized properties of galaxies that have been subjected to detailed study. The observed range for each feature is given, where known, and the actual values or descriptions are given for two examples of well-observed galaxies, M 31 and NGC 185. As this table shows, the variety of features observed in galaxies is great. Many important facts about these features are not yet known.

The abbreviations used in Table 1.1 are commonly used astronomical terms, and they will be used throughout this book. They are defined as follows:

kpc: kiloparsec, 1,000 parsecs, or 3×10^{21} cm.

M_V: absolute visual magnitude, a measure of the intrinsic luminosity in terms of the apparent brightness in magnitudes if the object were 10 parsecs distant.

$B - V$: color in the standard three-color UBV system. Blue objects have $B - V$ small; red objects, large.

Spectral type: classification of spectrum according to temperature. Classes are O, B, A, F, G, K, and M in order of decreasing temperature.

$M_{H\,I}/M$: ratio of mass in the form of H I (neutral hydrogen) to total mass.

TABLE 1.1   PROPERTIES OF GALAXIES

VARIABLE	RANGE	M 31	NGC 185
Intrinsic diameter	1 to 50 kpc	50	2.9
Total luminosity	-8 to -25 in M_V	-20.0	-15.4
Mass	10^5 to 10^{12} suns	4×10^{11}	1.5×10^8
Color	$+0.2$ to $+1.1$ in $B - V$	$+0.9$	$+1.1$
Spectral type	A to K in blue	G5	G0
Chemical composition	Metal lines: weak to strong	Strong	Weak
Rotational symmetry	Present or absent	Present	Present
Nucleus	Present or absent	Present	Present
Spiral arms	Present or absent	Present	Absent
Central bar	Present or absent	Absent ?	Absent
Internal ring	Present or absent	Absent	Absent
External ring	Present or absent	Absent	Absent
Mean surface brightness	High to low	Moderately high	Moderately low
Smoothness of intensity gradient	Smooth to stepped or irregular	Stepped	Smooth
Dust	None to large amounts	Moderate amounts	Very little
Neutral gas	<0.01 to 0.30 in $M_{H\,I}/M$	0.013	<0.2
Excited gas	None to dominating the spectrum	Some	None

4   Other terms used in the following chapters are explained in two other books of this series: "The Sun and Stars," by J. C. Brandt, and "The Galaxy," by H. Weaver.

✳ 2 ✳

form
and
classification

A classification scheme generally must satisfy two criteria to be successful. First, it must act as a shorthand means of identification of salient features of the object. Second, it should have some much more fundamental physical significance, so that it divides the objects into real groups, the understanding of which promotes and furthers the understanding of the objects themselves. In the case of the classification of galaxy forms, the principal schemes that have been proposed so far satisfy both of these criteria to varying degrees. The biggest differences between them seem to be differences of elaboration.

THE HUBBLE CLASSIFICATION

The most generally used classification scheme of galaxies is one of those first proposed, by Edwin Hubble in 1926. His classification is based entirely on the visual appearance of a galaxy on a

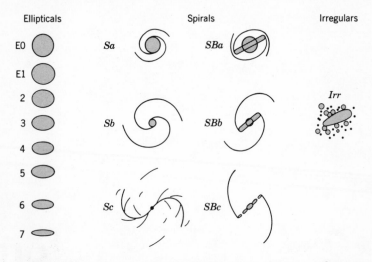

FIGURE 2.1   Types of galaxies according to the Hubble classification system.

photographic plate. In order to be effectively used, the classification requires that a galaxy's image be large enough so that individual features can be discerned. Hubble divided galaxies into three general categories: the elliptical galaxies, the spiral galaxies, and the irregular galaxies. His classification scheme consists of subdivisions of these three groups (Figure 2.1).

Elliptical Galaxies. The galaxies which Hubble termed elliptical were defined as those with complete rotational symmetry. They are figures of revolution with two equal principal axes and a third axis that is smaller, usually, and is the axis of rotation (at least geometrically if not actually physically). The elliptical galaxies contain practically no dust or young blue O- and B-type supergiant stars, very little gas, and no irregularities or patchiness. A few elliptical galaxies show emission lines of forbidden oxygen and, occasionally, Hα in emission. The isophotes of elliptical galaxies are all similar ellipses, and the surface brightness decreases according to a common general law. Globular clusters are often conspicuous attendants to elliptical galaxies.

The subdivision of elliptical galaxies which Hubble introduced is a subdivision according to the apparent (not necessarily the real) ratio of major to minor axis. An elliptical galaxy is designated by E, followed by a number n, which equals $10(a-b)/a$, where a is the major axis and b the minor axis of the visible image. Thus an elliptical galaxy with a circular outline is an $E0$ galaxy, while that with a more elliptical outline might be an $E5$ or an $E6$. Hubble found that there were no elliptical galaxies flatter than $E7$, so the maximum possible major–minor-axis ratio is $10/3$.

Spiral Galaxies. A large number of galaxies exhibit a spiral structure, with two or more spiral arms arranged symmetrically about a nuclear region. Hubble divided the spiral class into two broad groups, the first being the "normal" spirals, the arms of which originate at the center of the galaxy, and the second being the "barred" spirals, the arms of which originate at the ends of a luminous bar symmetrical about the center. Within these two broad categories the spiral galaxies are arranged according to three correlated criteria: the relative size of the nuclear region, the tightness of winding of the spiral arms, and the degree of resolution of arms into patchiness.

The first subclass is the Sa galaxy, which is characterized by a very large, amorphous nuclear area and extremely tightly wound spiral arms. The arms are usually smooth, defined primarily by absorption lanes; there may or may not be arms of luminous matter exterior to these absorption arms.

The *Sb* galaxies are distinguished by a wide dispersion of appearance. Normally they have moderately large nuclear regions, moderately loosely wound arms (usually two), and a fair degree of resolution into patches in the outer parts of the arms. The inner parts of the arms are often defined only by deep absorption regions.

Sc galaxies are distinguished by the extremely inconspicuous nature of their nuclear regions and the fact that their spiral arms are very loose and well resolved into lumpiness. The resolution of the arms can be detected for galaxies as far away as 150 million parsecs. Normally the *Sc* galaxies have two arms which wind outward to about one-half of a full turn, at which location they have almost become tangent to the galaxy.

Barred spiral galaxies are divided into three classes in the same way that normal spiral galaxies are; they range from *SBa* to *SBc*, depending on the size of the nuclear region, the tightness of the arms, and the resolution of the arms. In general they are very much like normal spiral galaxies; they have the same range of luminosities, sizes, spectra, and distribution in the sky. The conspicuously barred spirals are considerably less common than the normal spirals, but it has recently been shown that a large percentage of spiral galaxies have at least a hint of a barred structure. Hubble's original classification did not take into account this continuity of types between normal and barred spirals.

Irregular galaxies lack rotational symmetry, are highly resolved into patchiness, and are devoid of recognizable pattern. They were designated *Irr* in the Hubble scheme.

HUBBLE'S REVISED CLASSIFICATION

In 1936, Hubble revised slightly his classification of galaxies to take into account his more recent studies of their forms. He made four important changes to the classification scheme. The first was in relation to the *E7* galaxies. He found that when detailed photometry of *E7* galaxies was carried out, their isophotes were not perfectly elliptical in shape but were pointed at the ends (see

Figure 2.2). Hubble decided that such a galaxy could not properly
be called an elliptical galaxy and introduced a new classification,
which he called S0. This new class included the old $E7$ galaxies as
well as several newly recognized types of galaxies that he believed

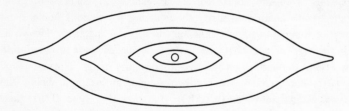

FIGURE 2.2   Isophotes of an $E7$ galaxy, showing how outer isophotal
lines are sometimes not perfectly elliptical.

to be distinguished by a disklike shape without spiral structure.
Hubble pictured the S0 galaxies as an intermediate type between the
most flat elliptical galaxies and the Sa galaxies.

Hubble also introduced in 1936 his famous tuning-fork diagram
(Figure 2.3), which organized the classification in visual sequence.
He felt that it was possible that the tuning-fork diagram and his

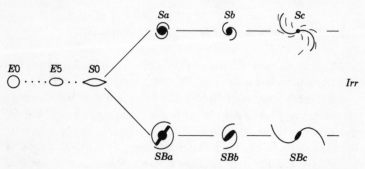

FIGURE 2.3   The Hubble tuning-fork diagram, illustrating relationships
between the types of galaxies.

classification were evolutionary, but it is now known that this is
unlikely (see Chapter 11).

The third introduction into his revised classification was the concept of the mixed spiral, a galaxy with a small bar in the nuclear region but otherwise a normal spiral.

Hubble's fourth change was to propose an entirely new class of galaxies, a subtype of the irregular galaxy. In general, irregular galaxies are characterized by their having no obvious nucleus, no rotational symmetry, and emission lines in the spectrum. However, Hubble recognized that the irregular galaxies were divided into two types depending on the resolution of the image. Normal (type I) irregular galaxies are highly resolved, an example being the Largé Magellanic Cloud (LMC) (Chapter 6). Type II irregular galaxies, however, are very peculiar objects, not showing resolution but characterized by a great deal of obscuration and dust. The example Hubble chose to illustrate the characteristics of type II irregular galaxies is the galaxy M 82, now known to have recently experienced an immense explosive event which may well have altered its appearance so drastically that little of its original shape can be discerned. Type II irregular galaxies have not been extensively studied as yet, and so it is not known whether all of them can be explained in terms of a violent event of the type experienced by M 82.

SANDAGE'S REVISION OF THE HUBBLE CLASSIFICATION

The most recent extension of the Hubble classification of galaxies is that published by Sandage in 1960. Sandage's classification is based directly on that of Hubble but extends it to a large number of subclasses of galaxies. In particular, Sandage divided the S0 galaxies into three subgroups. The $S0_1$ galaxy is similar to an elliptical galaxy except for a flatter intensity gradient. This type of S0 galaxy, according to Sandage's classification, is characterized also by a fundamental thin plane, as in the case of spiral galaxies.

The second subtype of S0 galaxy in the Sandage classification is $S0_2$, similar to $S0_1$ except for the delicate structure in its outer portions, usually amounting to "steps" in the intensity profile of the outer envelopes. It may be that the structure is related to a change from an elliptical inner portion to a flat outer fundamental plane.

The $S0_3$ classification is similar, according to Sandage, to the $S0_1$ type but has a dark absorption lane in the central parts of the galaxy. Usually this absorption lane shows up on only one side of the central "lens," but for galaxies that are nearly face-on it is sometimes possible to trace it completely around the nuclear region. Sandage believes that there is a transition from the $S0_3$ type to the Sa type of galaxy, and some galaxies classified as $S0_3$ have the hint of an interior spiral arm structure.

Many galaxies classified by Sandage as S0 are exceedingly peculiar and do not fit into these three classification subtypes at all. Some of these have absorption lanes arranged in a very irregular pattern, and others show evidence of double nuclei, multiple axes of rotation, square central isophotes, or other peculiarities. In a certain sense, then, the S0 classification has been applied to any galaxy that appears to have an underlying distribution of stars similar to that of an elliptical galaxy but is peculiar in one of a number of different ways.

Sandage has also divided the spiral galaxies into subclassifications, according to whether they are characterized by a *ring forma-*

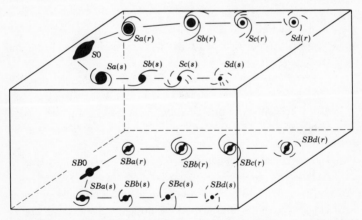

FIGURE 2.4   Sandage's box diagram, showing divisions into spiral (s) and ring (r) subgroups. The entire volume of the box is populated with intermediate types.

tion or not. This distinction applies to both normal spirals and barred spirals and is illustrated graphically in Figure 2.4. As the figure shows, Sandage has added a type which is intermediate between type *Sc* and *Irr* I. This he calls type *Sd*, following Shapley's use.

DE VAUCOULEURS'S CLASSIFICATION SCHEME

A further development of the basic Hubble classification scheme is that proposed by De Vaucouleurs. He has attempted to take into account a wide variety of intermediate types, and has included many new subtypes and intermediate class notations. The elaborate scheme which De Vaucouleurs proposes has four principal features:

1. He allows for the galaxies that are intermediate between normal spiral galaxies and barred spiral galaxies. The normal spiral galaxies are classified *SA;* the barred spirals are classified *SB;* and intermediate objects which look as if they have a normal general structure but the hint of a bar are classified *SAB.*

2. De Vaucouleurs also allows for the presence or absence of a ring structure. This is designated with an (*r*) or an (*s*). Transition types between those with a clearly defined ring and those without are designated by an (*rs*).

   Outer ringlike structures, which are sometimes observed for early-type galaxies (that is, S0- or SA-type galaxies) are also taken into account. Those with such ring structure are denoted by an (*R*) preceding the main letter indicating the classification.

3. Intermediate steps between the main classifications are allowed. The three stages among the S0 galaxies are indicated as S0$^-$, S0^0, and S0$^+$. These form a transition between the *E* galaxies and the *SA* galaxies. Elliptical galaxies that are almost S0 galaxies are designated by S0/*E*. Further intermediate stages are used in the classification of spiral galaxies such that an *SA* galaxy which is intermediate between *SAa* and *SAb* is called an *SAab.* Those spiral galaxies that are intermediate between *Sd* and irregulars (*Im*) are denoted *Sm.*

4. The irregular galaxies are divided into two types, the *Im* type, typified by the Magellanic Clouds, and the *I0* type, typified by M 82 and those irregular galaxies which look more like S0 galaxies.

The application of De Vaucouleurs's classification to galaxies shows that a great deal of information about an individual galaxy, when known, can be given in brief form. It is found, however, that a certain amount of subjectivity exists, and not everyone classifies a given galaxy in the same way in this system.

The nearby spiral galaxy in Andromeda, M 31 (NGC 224), is classified by De Vaucouleurs as $SA(s)b$. The other nearby spiral M 33 (NGC 598) is classified by De Vaucouleurs as $SA(s)cd$. Another example is NGC 1318, which is classified $(R)SAB(rs)0/a$. Even for this very detailed and loose-fitting classification scheme, there are galaxies which do not fit and for which De Vaucouleurs

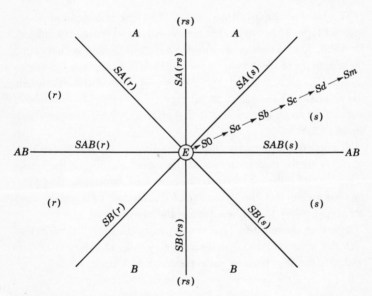

FIGURE 2.5　De Vaucouleurs's pinwheel diagram, a flat projection of his three-dimensional classification system.

has had to add a p, indicating peculiarities. The De Vaucouleurs scheme has been graphically illustrated by its author in the form of a pinwheel, reproduced in Figure 2.5.

In 1957 Morgan and Mayall suggested a classification of galaxies that is based primarily on the spectrum of the galaxy. Because the spectrum is, of course, a composite one, this classification depends on the portion of the spectrum examined and, too, on the portion of the galaxy for which the spectrum has been obtained. In the spectrographic classification developed in detail later by Morgan, the spectral region is blue and ultraviolet and the spectrum is for the nuclear region only, in most cases. The spectral type is classified in comparison with standard stars and is designated as either *a*, *af*, *f*, *fg*, *g*, *gk*, or *k*, according to which stellar spectral types dominate the spectrum.

The scheme employs three digits. The first is indicative of the spectral type. The second indicates whether the galaxy is elliptical, *E*, spiral, *S*, or irregular, *I*. The third digit is a number indicating the ellipticity of the image, following Hubble's numbers for elliptical galaxies. Morgan and Mayall, however, use this to designate the ellipticity of the image of all types of galaxies. An example of a classification on this scheme is that of M 31, which Morgan classifies as *kS5*.

The spectrographic classification of galaxies has contributed considerably to the understanding of the stellar makeup of the nuclei of galaxies of different types. It is particularly interesting that Morgan has found that the spectrum of the nucleus of a galaxy does not always follow the Hubble type of the galaxy.

A further classification type developed by Morgan, in connection with the identification of radio sources, is the *D* galaxy, which is related to the $S0_1$ classification in the Sandage scheme.

THE LUMINOSITY CLASSIFICATION

It was discovered by Van den Bergh that the appearance (surface brightness, nature of spiral arms) of *Sb*, *Sc*, and *Irr* galaxies is related to their absolute luminosities. He devised a luminosity classification scheme to take advantage of this fact. By comparing a galaxy at an unknown distance with Van den Bergh's standards, it is possible to determine its approximate absolute magnitude and thus its distance. The classes are designated by Roman numerals, with I the most luminous and V the least. The absolute magnitudes range from −20.0 for a class I galaxy to −16 for a class IV–V.

APPARENT AND TRUE FORMS

The classification systems which have been worked out are based on two-dimensional images of galaxies and therefore do not necessarily characterize the true three-dimensional form of the object. There is no easy way of constructing a three-dimensional model from the two-dimensional plate, but by using dynamical arguments or statistics it is possible to obtain information on true forms of galaxies.

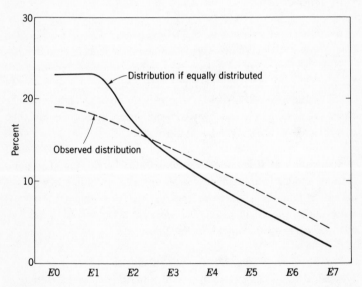

FIGURE 2.6   A comparison of the observed distribution (among subtypes) of elliptical galaxies with a curve calculated for a sample with equal numbers of true axial ratios.

Distribution of Orientation of Ellipticals. At present there is no way to know whether an elliptical galaxy is viewed edge-on or face-on or in between. For instance, an *E*0 galaxy might be spherical or it might be a very eccentric ellipsoid viewed face-on. Eventually, it is hoped that exceedingly high-precision photometry might be able to distinguish between these possibilities, but so far the problem has only been attacked statistically. Hubble showed many years ago that if you assume that there is an equal number of elliptical galaxies with true ellipticities in each class from *E*0 to *E*7, you very closely reproduce the observed statistical distribution of galaxies among these different classes. Figure 2.6 illustrates this close confirmation between the observed and the expected distribution. We conclude, therefore, that elliptical galaxies are pretty much evenly divided in true ellipticity between those that are spherical at one extreme and those that have a ratio of axes of 0.3 at the other extreme.

Distribution of Orientation of S0 Galaxies. A similar examination of the S0 galaxies shows very poor agreement between the observed distribution of ellipticity and the assumption that they are widely different in their true form. However, if it is assumed that all S0 galaxies are flat, with a ratio of axes of $b/a = 0.3$, then the observed distribution can be well reproduced. We conclude then that S0 galaxies are essentially all flat objects.

Distribution of Orientation of Spiral Galaxies. For spiral galaxies a result similar to that found for S0 galaxies is obtained, with the exception that there are more very flat galaxies among the spirals than among the S0 galaxies. The very flattest observed spiral galaxies have a ratio of axes of less than 0.1.

The Direction of the Tilt of Spiral Galaxies. There has been a great deal of discussion of means of determining the direction of tilt of spiral galaxies that are not seen face-on. The best criterion used so far is the obscuration that is silhouetted against the nucleus of galaxies. Unfortunately, galaxies for which this criterion can be used are rare, but for the dozen or so galaxies that have been studied so far it is concluded that in all cases the direction of tilt is such that the spiral arms of the galaxy are trailing. Lindblad has used the distribution of color and luminosity in galaxies as arguments in some cases for an opposite orientation to that derived from study of the obscuration.

Tilt. The angle between the line of sight and the plane of the disk of a spiral galaxy is called the *tilt* of the galaxy. This angle is very difficult to establish with high accuracy, even for the very easiest cases. The reasons for the difficulty are four in number:

1. The true three-dimensional shape of a given spiral galaxy is unknown to any high degree of accuracy.
2. Absorption effects, particularly in the central regions, distort the image of the object in a way which cannot always be taken into account and recognized immediately.
3. The arms of spiral galaxies often are not geometrically perfect. Some spiral galaxies have arms that do not match on either side; the arrangement of luminosity is not symmetrical about the center of the galaxy. Other spiral galaxies have arms that are not even in the normal plane of the galaxy but seem to deviate several degrees from this plane.
4. Some galaxies, such as M 33, have possibly bar-shaped nuclei, confusing the apparent tilt of the object.

The estimation of the tilt of galaxies is based normally on the ratio of the minor to the major axis of the projected image. However, some galaxies for which this has been done with care have been studied on long- and short-exposure plates, and it has been found that the derived ratio of axes is a function of distance from the center of the galaxy. This leads to a certain amount of inconclusiveness in establishment of the correct angle of tilt. The tilts of only a few galaxies have been determined with high accuracy.

❋ **3** *❋* **integrated
properties**

Because most galaxies are too far away to be resolved into individual stars, much of our knowledge regarding galaxies concerns their integrated properties. The most important of these are the integrated luminosities, the total color, the integrated spectra, and the systematic radial velocity.

INTEGRATED MAGNITUDES

The total absolute luminosity of a galaxy is determined by measuring its integrated magnitude and by knowing its distance. The integrated magnitudes of galaxies are not easy to obtain because the faint outer extensions of most galaxies are difficult to include accurately in the total. Two methods have been used to obtain integrated magnitudes accurately. The first is to measure the apparent magnitude through a series of diaphragms of increasing radius and then to extrapolate to some defined limit. The second is to measure isophotes for the entire galaxy and then to integrate over these isophotes for the total magnitude. These measurements have been made either photographically or photoelectrically for several thousand galaxies. Most of the recent photoelectric work has used the standard *UBV* color system, and it has led to accurate magnitudes and colors for a large number of the brighter galaxies. In all cases measurements have been made with a variety of diaphragm sizes so that an estimate of the total integrated magnitude could be determined.

Total Magnitudes. Determining total magnitudes for galaxies by means of applying corrections to measured magnitudes is a very difficult process. Its importance is very great because any systematic effect in the corrections applied will invalidate any conclusion regarding cosmology that might be drawn. This correction can be very large, because of the very extensive faint outer portions that many galaxies have. For instance, NGC 3379 seems to have a diameter as estimated on 48-in. Schmidt plates of about 120 sec, while measurements made with a highly sensitive isophotometer can be carried out to diameters as large as 500 sec. Errors involved in the total magnitude of a galaxy for which this outer extension is not taken into account can amount to almost 0.5 mag. Therefore, since virtually all published photoelectric measures omit the outer part of each galaxy, these measures must be corrected and standardized.

The first task is to establish a definition of the diameter of a galaxy. When that is established and properly defined, the total magnitude can easily be obtained by integrating all luminosity out to that diameter. There are two ways of identifying the diameter of a galaxy. The first is to assume an intensity curve that is taken as standard and true for all galaxies. Then, the intensity curve is extrapolated out beyond observed points to the distance where the intensity reaches zero. The diameter thus defined is not necessarily realistic, because of the extrapolation involved, but it is a well-defined diameter. Not all the proposed intensity curves for galaxies can be used for such extrapolations, however, because some, for instance Hubble's, imply an infinite diameter and therefore an infinite total intensity for the galaxy. One interpolation formula for galaxies that does lead to a finite size and total luminosity is that of De Vaucouleurs (see Chapter 4).

A second method of establishing a total magnitude is one that does not require any extrapolation or assumption regarding the appropriate intensity curve for the galaxy. This is the method of identifying the diameter of a galaxy as the size out to a particular uniform isophote. This is essentially a means of measuring sizes of galaxies out to particular values of star density, as the star density is directly related to the surface brightness (under conditions of similar luminosity functions for stars). Sandage measured diameters of hundreds of galaxies out to a limiting surface brightness of 22.6 mag, about 0.6 mag below the sky background value for his plates. Later, he extrapolated beyond the observed diameters to a fainter isophote, 25.0 mag/(sec of arc)^2. At this level, he estimated that the apparent diameter is 2.5 times greater than the measured diameter.

INTEGRATED COLORS

Total integrated colors for galaxies have been measured both photographically and photoelectrically. The photographic measures in most cases have been rather uncertain because of the uncertainty in the calibration of photographic photometry. The most careful photographically determined colors are those of Holmberg. For some of the exceedingly low-surface-brightness members of the local group of galaxies, his photographically determined integrated colors are the best available.

Photoelectric measures of colors, where the measurements can be taken in different colors nearly simultaneously, are a great deal faster and more easily obtained. Most of the compilations of photoelectric magnitudes of galaxies have also included photoelectric colors. The most recent and most uniform group of such measurements comes from the compilation of colors measured in the *UBV* system by various investigators. These accurate measures have shown that galaxies have a wide variety of colors and that the integrated color is correlated with the type of galaxy. Figure 3.1

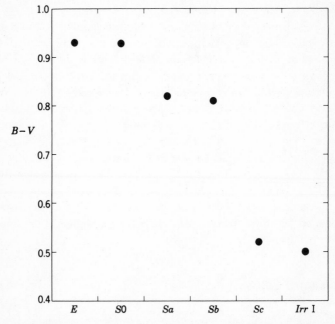

FIGURE 3.1   Mean colors of galaxies as a function of type.

shows how the types of galaxies are correlated with colors, and Figure 3.2 gives the mean-color plot for galaxies of various types and shows how the spread looks in each type.

Plate 1   NGC 3384, an *SB0* galaxy in the nearby Leo group, photographed with the Lick Observatory 120-in. telescope.

Plate 2   NGC 3593, an *S0* peculiar galaxy in the Leo group (120-in. photograph).

Plate 3   NGC 4303, an *SBc* galaxy in the Virgo cluster (120-in. photograph).

Plate 4   A portion of the Large Magellanic Cloud, photographed with the Uppsala Schmidt. 30 Doradus is in the upper left corner.

The understanding of the integrated colors of galaxies depends
upon their interpretation in terms of color-magnitude diagrams

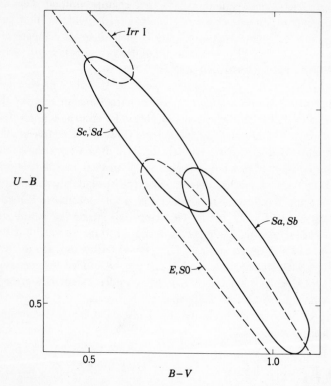

FIGURE 3.2 Two-color diagram, showing range of observed colors of various types of galaxies.

and luminosity functions. The spread observed in the color-color diagram for various types of galaxies indicates a spread of mean stellar content. Theoretically, one could set certain limits on the stellar content of a galaxy from its UBV measurements. However, this has not yet been done, mainly because of the indeterminacy of any result due to the wide bandpass of the *UBV* filters.

When narrower bandpass filters are used to measure integrated colors and intensities of galaxies, a more unique solution to the problem of the stellar content can be realized. Recent work by Wood has allowed a comparison between photoelectric integrated measurements and various hypothetical color-magnitude diagrams and luminosity functions.

INTERNAL REDDENING AND ABSORPTION

It is possible to make corrections to the total magnitude and the integrated color of the galaxy for the reddening and absorption caused by dust internally in the galaxy. However, it is a very difficult correction to make accurately because of the large spread in intrinsic colors of galaxies. By treating a statistical sample of galaxies, De Vaucouleurs has determined empirically that it is possible to estimate the amount of reddening and internal absorption in a galaxy from its *UBV* colors. He compared galaxies of a uniform type but of varying angles of inclination in order to establish the amount of absorption and reddening found on the average in each galaxy. Such statistical determinations can be applied to individual galaxies to correct for internal absorption effects, but they are not of high accuracy for an individual object because of the probable wide variation among galaxies of a particular type in the amount of dust present.

SPECTRA

The integrated spectra of galaxies have been studied in a number of ways in an attempt to establish the nature of their stellar content. It is a very difficult task; exposures are long, and the interpretation of the composite spectrum is complicated. The very low surface brightness of galaxies means that spectra only of the central nuclear areas are obtainable in most cases, and therefore spectroscopic studies are quite limited in scope. The worst observational problem is the contamination of a spectrum of a galaxy by the sky background. The limit to the faintness that can be reached is set by the night sky brightness, which at favorable locations is correlated with the solar cycle. For that reason, spectra of very faint galaxies in the past have been obtained only during solar minimum. In the future, by using image converters and by subtraction of the sky electronically, this problem should be alleviated somewhat. It is hoped that extraterrestrial observations will also become feasible when large reflecting telescopes are orbited as astronomical satellites.

Spectrographic studies by Spinrad, Morgan, Deutsch, and others have resulted in several important conclusions. It is found that the strengths of the sodium D lines and of TiO molecular bands can indicate the prevalence of giant or dwarf late-type stars, for instance. The most luminous elliptical galaxies have spectra indicating an exceedingly rich population of red dwarfs, while less luminous elliptical systems do not show this anomaly. Also, the superluminous elliptical galaxies are usually not as metal-poor as the less luminous galaxies, according to metallic line strengths in their spectra. Much more detailed spectrographic research is possible with large telescopes and surely will provide important data in the future.

※ **4** ※

**content
and
structure**

Galaxies are made up of stars, gas, and dust. What kind of stars and how much gas and dust depends closely on the galaxy's type and its structure.

STELLAR CONTENT

Populations. The stellar population of a galaxy is clearly discernible only for the very nearest, well-resolved objects. For others, some idea of the kinds of stars present can be obtained from colors or spectra.

In 1944 Baade suggested that there are two types of stellar populations, which he called "population I" and "population II." Elliptical galaxies seemed to be entirely made up of population II stars, irregular galaxies entirely of population I stars, and spiral galaxies of both. Today it is considered rather superficial to speak of these population types, as the physically important features of stars (age, mass, composition) can now be discerned. It is known that Baade's population I is made up of young stars of high heavy-element abundance and population II of old stars of low heavy-element abundance. The two other possible combinations also exist, at least in other galaxies, so that the original division does not apply

TABLE 4.1   POPULATIONS I AND II

POPULATION I	POPULATION II
Open clusters	Globular clusters
H II regions	RR Lyrae variables
H I emission	W Virginis variables
OB associations	RV Tauri variables
classical cepheids	Planetary nebulae
Long period variables with $P > 200^d$	Long period variables with $P < 200^d$
Type II supernovae	Type I supernovae
Low-velocity stars	High-velocity stars

universally. For some purposes, however, the terminology is still used, and therefore a list of the membership of the two populations is given here (Table 4.1).

Color-Magnitude Diagrams. Only for the very nearest galaxies has it been possible to plot color-magnitude diagrams of individual stars. These have now been measured for the Large Magellanic Cloud (LMC), the Small Magellanic Cloud (SMC) (Chapter 6), M 31 (Chapter 8), Sculptor (Chapter 9), IC 1613, NGC 6822, Draco, and Ursa Minor (Chapter 7). The diagrams have led to the important discovery that *all* galaxies, regardless of type, contain old stars that must have ages of about 10^{10} years. Even the Magellanic Clouds, which are rich in gas and young stars and which were

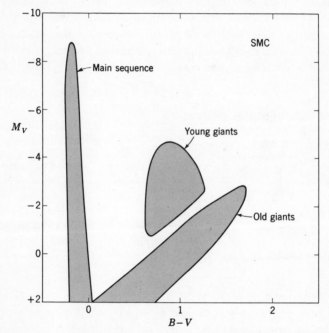

FIGURE 4.1   Schematic color-magnitude diagram of a portion of the Small Magellanic Cloud, based on photometry of individual stars. (After Arp.)

once thought to be young galaxies, have an underlying population of old stars showing up in the color-magnitude diagrams (Figure 4.1).

From the color-magnitude diagrams of the elliptical galaxies mentioned, it is possible to show that star formation occurred only during a relatively short interval about 10^{10} years ago, after which essentially no new stars formed. The gas and dust were either entirely used up or expelled from the system during this period of star formation.

Spiral galaxies seem to have a mixture of ages and compositions of stars, with the young stars concentrated in the spiral arms and the old stars spread out more smoothly. There is evidence, at least for our Galaxy itself, that the chemical composition of the stars in a spiral galaxy varies with position, the most heavy-element-rich stars being the most closely confined to the plane of the galaxy. Our Galaxy has been divided into four components, differing from each other in age, composition, and dynamical properties (Table 4.2).

TABLE 4.2   COMPONENTS OF THE GALAXY

COMPONENT	AGE OF YOUNGEST STARS, YR	COMPOSITION	TYPE OF ORBIT
Halo	$\sim 2 \times 10^{10}$	Metals very weak	Very eccentric
Subhalo	$\sim 10^{10}$	Metals weak	Moderately eccentric
Disk	$\sim 10^{9}$	Metals moderate	Nearly circular
Flat	~ 0	Metals strong	Circular

Colors and Spectra. Multicolor surface photometry and calibrated spectra have been used to explore the content of quite a large number of galaxies. Neither method has led to highly accurate quantitative results so far, because of the great difficulties of reconstructing details from an integrated measurement. Nevertheless, a number of important conclusions have been drawn from such data. For instance, from multicolor data on the galaxy M 32, the astronomers Baum and Roberts showed that the galaxy could be synthesized by a combination of a globular cluster population plus a large number of very cool red dwarf stars.

Table 4.3 and Figure 4.2 illustrate how Stebbins's and Whitford's multicolor photometry and Spinrad's spectrographic measures have led to a model of the stellar content of the nucleus of M 31. It is found that only old stars exist in the nuclear regions and that most (but not all) of the stars are metal-rich. Vast numbers of cool

TABLE 4.3   MODEL OF THE NUCLEUS OF M 31

TYPE OF OBJECT	PERCENT CONTRIBUTION TO TOTAL LIGHT	RELATIVE NUMBER OF STARS
K0 III stars	50	2.8
G0 V stars	10	7
M1 V stars	40	4,000

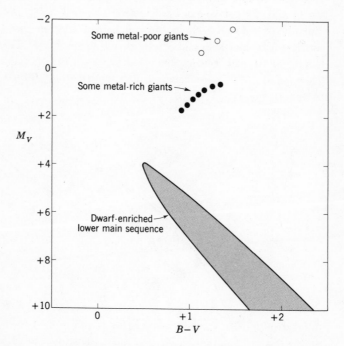

FIGURE 4.2   Schematic Hertzsprung-Russell diagram of M 31, based on spectra and integrated colors.

red dwarf stars also must exist there, many more than in the solar neighborhood, relative to the number of stars brighter than the sun. Generally speaking, most elliptical galaxies and the centers of many spirals have a similar content to that of M 31, although there is a noticeable variation in the numbers of metal-rich red dwarf stars. There is evidence that only the most luminous galaxies have a great excess of such stars.

Count-Brightness Ratio. For galaxies near enough to be partly re- solved, some indication of the stellar content can be obtained by comparing the counted star density to a particular limit to the total surface brightness. Usually only a small area of the galaxy is studied at a time, so that any variation of the count-brightness ratio over the face of the galaxy can be detected. This technique, which es- sentially tests for the luminosity function of stars in the galaxy, was first used by Baum and Schwarzschild to study the stellar con- tent of M 31 and its companion galaxy, NGC 205 (Chapter 7). They found a difference between the two that was attributed to a

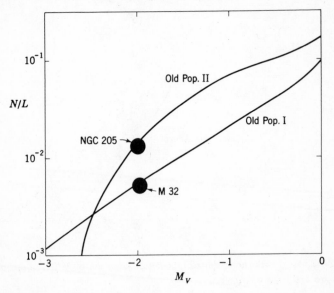

FIGURE 4.3   Count-brightness ratio, as a function of absolute magni- tude. (After Baum and Schwarzschild.)

difference in stellar content. The ratio for M 31 was like that for old population I stars, while that for NGC 205 was similar to that for old population II (metal-weak) stars (Figure 4.3).

Gas in Elliptical Galaxies. Since gas is characteristic of a population I-type environment, it is not surprising that very little gas has been detected in elliptical galaxies. The extensive Mt. Wilson–Lick Observatory survey of radial velocities of galaxies showed that approximately 15 per cent of all elliptical galaxies have emission lines of ionized oxygen (at λ3727), indicating the presence of some gas in the nuclei. The intensities of the emission lines range from barely detectable ones to very strong and very conspicuous ones. It is significant that no elliptical galaxies belonging to dense clusters of galaxies have emission lines at all. This is possibly due to the fact that collisions are fairly common in these dense clusters, and such collisions would sweep out all the gas in a galaxy.

A search for even fainter emission lines in the spectra of elliptical galaxies was carried out in 1960 by the astronomer Osterbrock, using the 200-in. telescope at Palomar. He found that approximately one out of six galaxies observed have very broad, very faint emission lines at λ3727. The detection was limited by the fine structure of the spectrum due to the absorption lines, many of which are blended.

An example of an elliptical galaxy with a detectable gas content studied by Osterbrock is NGC 4278, a typical $E1$ elliptical galaxy. Figure 4.4 shows schematically what the emission line looks like for

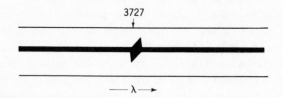

3727

—— λ ——→

FIGURE 4.4   Schematic spectrum of the elliptical galaxy NGC 4278, showing central emission feature.

this galaxy. It is inclined in a way indicating rotation of the gas cloud involved. At the center the emission line is very broad, indicating high turbulent velocities. Measurements indicate that the spread in velocity at the center is between 600 and 800 km/sec, and from the shape and size of the line it is concluded that the gas is spread out in an approximately circular distribution around the nucleus of the galaxy. It is not highly flattened, as might have been expected from the very noticeable rotation of this gas cloud. The turbulent velocity is highest at the center and becomes smaller outwards from the center reaching values near zero at the edge. The total size of the gas cloud is estimated to be about 200 parsecs, indicating that it is somewhat larger than a typical H II region in our Galaxy, but not very much. In addition to the $\lambda 3727$ line, six other emission lines are measurable in the spectrum of this galaxy, the others all being very much less intense than $\lambda 3727$. The relative intensities of the lines are very much like those in the Orion nebula in our Galaxy, and they indicate that the hydrogen-oxygen ratio is about the same as in the sun, if the temperature is about $10,000°K$.

One of the most puzzling features of the gas clouds occasionally found in elliptical galaxies' nuclei is the high turbulent motion, which would be expected to have been damped out in a relatively short time. It is concluded that energy must be injected into the gas in some way, either gravitationally or radiatively. The total mass of the gas is between 10^4 and 10^6 times that of the sun, and its density is an approximate 10 to 300 electrons/cm^3. The ionization mechanism is not understood completely, but it may be that the high velocity dispersion in the gas dissipates enough energy to keep it ionized. It also may be that there are a few hot blue stars in the elliptical galaxy, such as are occasionally found in globular clusters of our Galaxy, and these might have enough ultraviolet light to ionize any gas present and to give it large turbulent motions.

Although extensively searched for, no neutral hydrogen has been detected in elliptical galaxies so far. The upper limit to the amount of neutral hydrogen in an elliptical galaxy is approximately 0.1 percent.

Gas In Spiral and Irregular Galaxies. From the extensive survey of spectra of galaxies made at Mt. Wilson and at Lick, it is found that almost all *Sb*, *Sc*, and *Irr* galaxies have emission lines. A few *Sa* galaxies also show conspicuous emission. The irregular galaxies have the strongest lines and therefore the highest proportion of excited gas to stars. Generally the gas fraction decreases steadily towards earlier galactic types, from *Sc* to *Sa* and from *SBc* to *SBb*.

It has been shown by Burbidge and Burbidge that the gas in galaxies is distributed differently according to the type of galaxy, the gas being distributed most widely in irregular galaxies. For Sb and Sa galaxies, only a small area of the galaxy shows strong emission lines. Also, the excitation is higher in irregular galaxies than in any other types. The irregulars with nuclei have very large amounts of gas in these nuclei, and therefore there must be many high-luminosity stars there. SBc and SBb galaxies have lots of ionized gas in the nuclei, but only some of the Sb and Sc showed this. The degree of excitation of the gas varies within the classification groups and also within individual galaxies. Generally, it is found that the effective temperature is always on the order of 10,000°K and the electron density is less than 1,000/cm³. An interesting result of the study by the Burbidges is that the ratio of the strengths of the Hα line and the line of ionized nitrogen at $\lambda6583$ is different in different parts of galaxies. The ratio Hα/6583 decreases inwards in Sb and Sa galaxies with large nuclear bulges from approximately 3, which is the usual ratio for H II regions in our Galaxy, to approximately 0.1. This means that either the ratio of the number of hydrogen atoms to the number of nitrogen atoms decreases inwards, or else the mechanism of ionization and excitation in the interior of these galaxies is different from that in the outer portions; that is, it is not radiative, and the effective temperatures there are very much higher than normal, between 20,000 and 40,000°K.

In addition to spectrographic evidence regarding the nature, amount, and location of gas in spiral and irregular galaxies, a number of studies by filter photography methods have been carried out. Normally an interference filter centered on the line of Hα is used to obtain a photograph which shows only the objects emitting at this wavelength. Figure 4.5 shows an example of such a photograph for a spiral galaxy and illustrates how the emission regions, that is, the excited gas clouds, congregate along spiral arms. The result of a recent study of large numbers of such filter Hα photographs of galaxies is that the gas in Sc and irregular galaxies is widely distributed all the way from the center to the outermost portions, while the gas in Sb and Sa galaxies is more narrowly distributed, concentrated to the intermediate and outer arms. It also has been found that Hα regions are distributed along and across the arm in very much the same way as the underlying stars. The cross-sectional density of stars across an arm is no different from the cross-sectional density of Hα regions. This is rather surprising

NGC 613

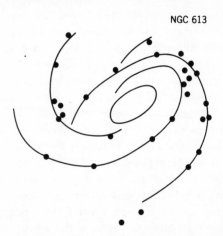

FIGURE 4.5　The location of emission regions (Hα) in the spiral galaxy NGC 613, showing their association with the spiral arms.

in light of the fact that the gas clouds must be illuminated by extremely young stars and therefore indicate areas of stellar formation, whereas the underlying star population is on the average very much older. Apparently an arm maintains its identity for a long period in this way. It is further interesting that some spiral galaxies have gas highly asymmetrically distributed. Figure 4.6 shows the distribution of H II regions in the galaxy NGC 3351, which has excited and ionized gas only in one-half of it.

The neutral gas content of galaxies can be studied by means of the 21-cm radio line. Very extensive work on nearby galaxies has been carried out and is described in Chapter 13.

DUST CONTENT

Dust is conspicuous in many galaxies because of the dark absorption lanes that it causes. These are particularly conspicuous for galaxies seen at large tilt angles or nearly edge-on, where the dust,

which is usually confined to the plane of rotation of the galaxy, is
seen silhouetted against the bright spiral arms of the galaxy. It is

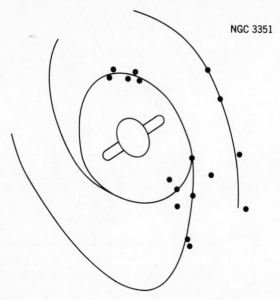

NGC 3351

FIGURE 4.6   Hα emission regions in NGC 3351, which has excited gas
only on one side.

found that the dust content of galaxies varies greatly from galaxy
to galaxy and within each classification type. There seems to be a
lack of dust in elliptical galaxies, except for a very few anomalous
objects. In spiral galaxies dust lanes are very conspicuous near the
nuclear bulge area and become less conspicuous outward from
there. This does not necessarily mean that the dust is concentrated
toward these more central locations. While this may in fact be the
case, it is also possible that the effect is due to the ease with which
the dust lanes are detected when a bright, smooth background of
starlight is available.

The total amount of dust in a dust region or dust lane in a galaxy
can be estimated from the amount of extinction of star light that it
causes. From studies of dust clouds in our Galaxy, it has been

shown that the mean density of a dust cloud is given by the following approximate formula

$$\bar{\rho} = \frac{4/3\Delta m \; a\rho_G}{1.086 \; Qd}$$

where Δm = amount of extinction due to the cloud
a = radius of the dust grains
ρ_G = density of the dust grains
d = depth of the cloud
Q = efficiency factor

Generally the values for a, Q, and ρ_G are taken to be approximately 3×10^{-5}, 2, and 1, respectively, in cgs units. Thus for a roughly spherical dust cloud of radius r, the mass is given by the formula

$$M = 8 \times 10^{-5} \; \Delta m \; r^2$$

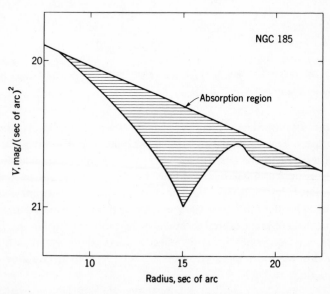

FIGURE 4.7   Profile of an inner part of the galaxy NGC 185, showing the dip in brightness attributed to a dust cloud.

Masses for dark nebulae or dust lanes in other galaxies are found generally to lie in the range of 10 to 100 times the mass of the sun if discrete clouds are considered. The total dust content of galaxies has been found to be as much as 0.05 percent of the total mass of the galaxy.

Two indirect methods of detecting and measuring the dust content of galaxies are by studying the polarization of objects in the galaxy and by studying the general reddening of individual stars and clusters. Particularly, for globular clusters in galaxies such as M 31, polarization measurements have shown that the dust in the spiral arms is aligned, probably by a magnetic field, along the spiral arms. For some galaxies, for instance, the Small Magellanic Cloud, the dust content is very difficult to detect except by polarization measurements or by measurements of the general reddening of individual stars. In the case of the Small Magellanic Cloud, reddening indicates that there is a very small but not negligible dust content, though discrete dust clouds are not detectable by visual examination of photographs.

STRUCTURE

Elliptical Galaxies. The structure of elliptical galaxies can be studied by means of photometry of the image or, for the nearest systems, by star counts. Photometric investigations lead to values of the intensity, either in absolute or relative units, as a function of distance from the center along specified axes. This is then compared with theoretical profiles derived under various sets of assumptions.

In the past, studies of the structure of elliptical galaxies led to derivations of empirical interpolation formulas. It was found, first by Hubble, that all elliptical galaxies have a similar structure, differing only in central intensity and scale. Hubble's interpolation formula was of the form,

$$I = I_0 \left(\frac{r}{a} + 1 \right)^{-2}$$

where I_0 = central intensity
r = distance from the center
a = a scale parameter

Other, somewhat different, formulas have been proposed by subsequent workers. All these interpolation "laws" for elliptical galaxies agree rather well with the observed distribution of light or stars except in the central regions and in the very outermost parts.

In recent years theoretical models of elliptical galaxies have been developed, and now comparisons of observations can be made with them. Figure 4.8 illustrates such a comparison and shows how well

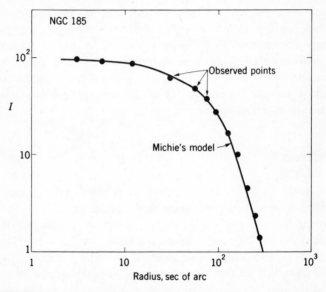

FIGURE 4.8   A comparison of the observed profile of NGC 185 with Michie's theoretical model of the galaxy.

the models agree with reality. From fitting with observations it is possible to gain considerable information, including an idea of the relative numbers of different kinds of orbits the stars of the galaxy possess, as well as of the density and mass distribution within the galaxy.

Spiral Galaxies. For spiral galaxies, including S0 types, there is considerable variety in structure. Generally, the spirals can be thought of as consisting of three parts. In the center is an "ellipsoidal" component, the nuclear "bulge," with structure and content similar to elliptical galaxies. Outside of this is a "flat" component, with a decrease of luminosity outward that is approximately exponential. Figure 4.9 shows an S0 galaxy that is made up of these two components of structure.

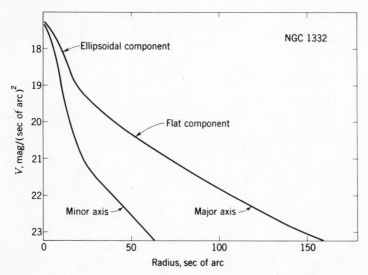

FIGURE 4.9   Profile of major and minor axes of an S0 galaxy, NGC 1332.

The third component of spiral galaxies is the spiral arm structure that is embedded in the "flat" component. Usually, though conspicuous in photographs, the arms contribute little to the overall light and are inconspicuous features of the intensity distribution. Figure 4.10 shows a photometric profile for a galaxy with unusually prominent arms. Even for it the arms are seen to provide only minor fluctuations in the curve.

The structure of few irregular galaxies has been studied. For the Magellanic Clouds and two or three others, it is found that the mean-intensity distribution is roughly like that of the "flat" component of a spiral galaxy.

42

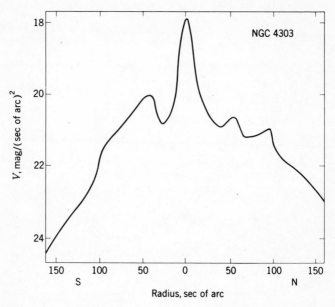

FIGURE 4.10   Profile of the spiral galaxy NGC 4303, determined from direct photoelectric measures.

❋ 5 ❋

**masses
of galaxies**

The total mass of a galaxy can be measured in one of four different ways. Each method is limited to galaxies of certain types or galaxies in certain configurations, and each has its theoretical and observational difficulties. Table 5.1 gives a summary of the methods, limitations, and problems involved. The results for masses of galaxies determined by the various methods have not always agreed, and there is therefore some uncertainty in regard to both the actual masses of some galaxies and the applicability of some of the methods.

TABLE 5.1   METHODS OF MASS DETERMINATION

METHOD	LIMITED TO	DIFFICULTIES
Internal rotation	Nearby mostly late-type galaxies	Lower limit, outer parts neglected
Double-galaxy orbital motion	Double galaxies (true binaries)	Must be statistical (projection)
Virial theorem in clusters	Clusters	Statistical; many assumptions
Velocity dispersion	Bright galaxies	Many assumptions

INTERNAL ROTATION METHOD

Probably the most reliable method of determining the mass of an individual galaxy is the determination and subsequent interpretation of its rotation curve. When the complete curve of the velocity as a function of distance from the center of a galaxy is known, a model of the mass distribution can be found that fits this curve, and this model can then be integrated to obtain the total mass in the system. For the nearest galaxies the rotation curve is obtained by measuring individual spectra of many emission nebulosities in the galaxy. This method requires a large amount of observation time with a telescope of large scale. The galaxies M 31, M 33, M 81, and the Large Magellanic Cloud have all been studied in this way.

For those galaxies of large angular extent, it is possible to measure the rotation curve by means of the neutral hydrogen line at

21 cm (radio wavelengths). This method is discussed later (Chapter 13). Using two adjacent radio telescopes as an interferometer has enabled radio astronomers to determine rotation curves at 21 cm for about a dozen galaxies. Figure 5.1 compares the rotation curves for a galaxy determined optically with one determined by radio means. The rather large differences in some portions of the curve are apparently due to observational errors of a type not yet understood.

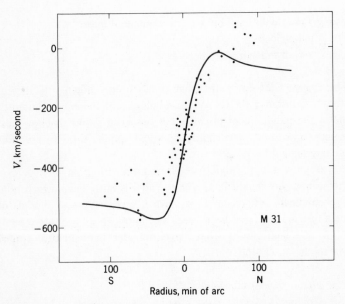

FIGURE 5.1   Velocity curves for M 31. The line is that obtained from neutral hydrogen. Dots are velocities of individual optical emission regions.

For more distant galaxies, optical composite spectra can be used. Most of the work of this type has been done by the astronomers E. Burbidge and G. Burbidge, who have obtained large numbers of small-scale spectra of distant Sb and Sc spirals. By measuring the Doppler displacement of individual emission lines at different distances from the center of certain galaxies, the Burbidges have been able to determine with considerable accuracy the complete rotation curves for such galaxies with only a few spectra.

To construct a model of a galaxy for which a rotation curve has been measured, one customarily argues that the gravitational force on any element of mass in the galaxy must be balanced by the centrifugal force due to rotation. That is,

$$f = \frac{v^2}{r}$$

where f = gravitational force on an element of mass
v = velocity
r = distance from the center

This neglects the "pressure" that comes from random velocities of stars, for instance, in the nuclear bulge, and therefore underestimates the gravitational force; but it has been found that for most galaxies measured, particularly late-type spirals, the effect of this force is negligible.

One must adopt a model of the mass distribution in a galaxy. Preferably, this should be a model which is fairly simple to handle mathematically. In recent years, five different types of models of mass distribution have been used, and although all are rather similar in the final results, they have different mathematical forms. The models are as follows:

1. Homogeneous ellipsoids
2. Nonhomogeneous plane circularly symmetrical disks
3. Nonhomogeneous ellipsoids
4. A series of nonhomogeneous ellipsoids
5. Spherical homoids

The results of the internal rotation method of determining masses of galaxies are summarized for several galaxies in Table 5.2. Most of the masses quoted there are in the range between 10^{10} and 10^{11} times the mass of the sun. Actually, these data refer to a highly selective group of galaxies, those giant galaxies that have large numbers of H II regions. The most massive galaxy listed in Table 5.2 is the nearby spiral M 31, which has a mass of 4×10^{11} $M_{\odot}$, which is approximately 8×10^{44} gm.

TABLE 5.2   SOME MASSES DETERMINED BY THE ROTATION-CURVE METHOD

GALAXY	TYPE	DISTANCE, Mpc	$M/M_\odot$	M/L
M 31	Sb	0.8	4×10^{11}	20
M 33	Sc	0.8	3×10^{10}	15
M 81	Sb	4	2×10^{11}	20
NGC 157	Sc	24	6×10^{10}	2
NGC 1068	Sb	10	$>3 \times 10^{10}$	2
NGC 2146	Sa	12	2×10^{10}	3
NGC 2903	Sc	7	4×10^{10}	5
NGC 3623	Sb	9	2×10^{11}	10
NGC 4594	Sb	14	2×10^{11}	3
NGC 5005	Sb	14	10^{11}	6
NGC 5055	Sb	8	6×10^{10}	2
NGC 5248	Sc	15	4×10^{10}	3

DOUBLE-GALAXY METHOD

Analogous to the determination of stellar masses by means of binary stars is the method of determining the total masses of galaxies by a statistical treatment of the orbits of binary galaxies. There are a large number of galaxies known that are apparently double, and many of these have radial velocities similar enough to suggest strongly that the two galaxies are at the same distance and are gravitationally connected as a double system. If one makes certain statistical samples of these galaxies and their radial velocities, one can arrive at statistical information about masses. The method requires the adoption of six important assumptions:

1. That double galaxies do not differ in any important way from normal field galaxies.
2. That the relative motion of the two galaxies is closed; that is, that the orbit of one about the other is not hyperbolic or parabolic.
3. That tidal effects between the two galaxies can be ignored.

4. That you can allow statistically for the projection effects due to the fact that we see their distance only in the plane of the sky and not in depth. This assumption is equivalent to saying that the orbits of double galaxies are oriented completely at random.

5. That the measured difference in velocity between the two members of the system can be assumed to be the projected orbital velocity for a circular orbit.

6. That the galaxies can be assumed to act as point masses.

This is a large number of assumptions, but when a sufficiently large sample of galaxies is used, it is not expected that these assumptions prove a major source of error. Observationally, one finds that the difference in velocity for double galaxies ranges from 0 to 650 km/sec, and the accuracy with which they can be measured with modern equipment is approximately ±50 km/sec. Table 5.3 lists results statistically derived for galaxies by Page, using the double-galaxy method.

TABLE 5.3   RESULTS OF DOUBLE-GALAXY METHOD

OBJECTS	MEAN $M/M_\odot$	M/L
All systems	3×10^{11}	40
S and *Irr*	4×10^{10}	3
E and S0	7×10^{11}	100

THE VIRIAL THEOREM IN CLUSTERS

The mean mass of galaxies in a cluster, or some statistical distribution of masses in a cluster, can be obtained if one is willing to assume that the virial theorem applies to the cluster. In order for this assumption to be justified, the cluster must consist of a stable group of point masses without any invisible mass such as might be provided by neutral gas or dust and without pairs or multiple groupings inside the cluster. Since the mass of a galaxy is apparently related to its total brightness in a direct way, normally one finds that most of the mass of a cluster is contained in only a few

of the brighter members of the cluster. Therefore one can apply
the virial theorem to a particular cluster of galaxies if one knows
the radial velocities of these bright members of the group.

The virial theorem says that

$$2E + \Omega = 0$$

where E is the time average of the kinetic energy and Ω is the time
average of the potential energy. The kinetic energy is determined
for a cluster from the radial velocities after an assumption is made
about the mean velocity of the group as a whole, and correction is
made for the component of the kinetic energy that is not seen in
the line of sight. The potential energy is estimated, in terms of the
unknown mass, from the separation of the individual members of
the galaxy from each other. In this estimation, allowance must be
made for the fact that we see only the projected separation in the
plane of the sky. The magnitudes of the galaxies for which radial
velocities are available must be measured as well, and an assumption
made about the variation in the mass-light ratio as a function of type
for the galaxies. When all of this is done, it is possible to substitute
all of these data (with the mass of the galaxies as an unknown) into

TABLE 5.4   SOME RESULTS FROM THE VIRIAL-THEOREM METHOD

GROUP	MEAN $M/M_\odot$	MEAN M/L
Stefan's Quintet	10^{12}	160
NGC 55 group	10^{12}	500
Pegasus (NGC 7619) group	$\sim 5 \times 10^{12}$	300
NGC 383 group	$\sim 5 \times 10^{12}$	260
Virgo cluster	$\sim 10^{13}$	600
Coma cluster	$\sim 10^{13}$	900

the virial theorem and to solve for the masses. Examples of results
for masses of galaxies in clusters are given in Table 5.4, where it is
seen that masses found are often very much larger than those found

by the methods discussed above. Also, the mass-light ratios are anomalously large, and there is indication that the discrepancy in both mass and mass-light ratio increases with the total size of the cluster. For the largest clusters, for instance Coma, the masses seem too large by a factor of 100 or more. It is not yet known why these anomalous results are obtained by application of the virial theorem, but it is suspected that one or more of the assumptions made is incorrect. Perhaps either the clusters involved are not truly stable or else the effect of smaller subgroupings is greater than we estimate. There may be large amounts of undetected matter between galaxies.

THE VELOCITY DISPERSION IN NUCLEI OF GALAXIES

An estimate of the total mass in an elliptical galaxy can be made by measuring the velocity dispersion in the nucleus from high-dispersion spectrograms. Normally it is assumed that all stars in such a system have approximately the same mass, and therefore the virial theorem can be applied. This means that

$$M \overline{v^2} + \Omega = 0$$

and

$$\Omega = -G \int_0^r \frac{M(r)\ dM}{r}$$

where M = total mass

R = total radius

Ω = potential energy of this system

G = constant of gravitation

r = instantaneous radius

$\overline{v^2}$ = average of the space velocities referred to the center of mass

It must be assumed that the mass-light ratio is constant and that Ω can be calculated from the light distribution measured photometrically. From models of elliptical galaxies it is known that most stars move in very eccentric orbits so that v^2 is approximately the same as the true velocity dispersion measured in the spectra. If the density in the nucleus is sufficiently large that close encounters occur, the orbits must be nearly random, so that the true velocity dispersion would be approximately three times the observed velocity distribution. If the nucleus is made up of a dense cluster of nuclear stars with small orbits, as may be the case in some elliptical galaxies, then the method cannot be used.

The results of the application of the virial theorem to two elliptical galaxies are very interesting. For the elliptical galaxy M 32, the resulting mass is 4×10^9 times the mass of the sun and the mass-light ratio is 13. For the galaxy NGC 3379, the mass is $10^{11} \times M_\odot$ and the mass-light ratio is 12. The close agreement in the mass-light ratios for these two elliptical galaxies suggests that they are very similar objects.

* **6** *

the
magellanic
clouds

Cosmologists assume, out of necessity, that the universe is homogeneous. They have taken for granted that galaxies in one location are not greatly different from those in any other location. This assumption may be quite wrong. There is already evidence that galaxies probably differ from each other in their chemical composition, and there is no guarantee that such a difference may not also occur in large sections of the universe.

Unfortunately, a galaxy must be quite nearby before its chemical composition can be measured accurately, and even for that for the nearest galaxies, the two Clouds of Magellan, there is a great deal of argument and mystery. The current intensive research on the properties of the Magellanic Clouds is partly motivated by the necessity to determine the effects of different chemical compositions on the fundamental extragalactic distance indicators. Many of these distance indicators are calibrated in the Magellanic Clouds, and thus much of the framework of distance determinations in the universe rests on observations of the Magellanic Clouds. Another reason for the recent emphasis on these galaxies is that they are the ones that can be studied in the most detail, and therefore we can learn a great deal about their content, organization, and probable evolution.

Although in the literature the two Clouds are often lumped together, their only physical connection is a large and very thin common envelope of neutral hydrogen. The content and integrated properties, as well as perhaps the distances, of the two galaxies are rather different. This chapter deals in considerable depth with the detailed properties of the Large Magellanic Cloud, as an example of a galaxy that has been the subject of extensive scrutiny. The Small Magellanic Cloud is described briefly at the end.

INTEGRATED PROPERTIES

Before dealing with the nature of the content, distance, and chemical composition of the Large Magellanic Cloud, it is useful to summarize the various properties that the galaxy as a whole has been found to have.

Integrated Magnitude. Because of its large angular extent, the total integrated apparent magnitude of the LMC is exceedingly

Plate 5   The central part of the Fornax dwarf galaxy, photographed
by Baade with the 200-in. Palomar telescope. (Photo courtesy Mt. Wilson
and Palomar Observatories.)

Plate 6   Three galaxies in the Virgo cluster, an *Sa* (upper left), an
SBc (bottom), and a dwarf elliptical (just barely visible at right center).
120-in. Lick photograph.

difficult to determine. Probably the most accurate measurement is that made in 1959 by Elsasser, who used a wide-field telescope with a photoelectric photometer to obtain surface brightness and colors for the Cloud and derived a total magnitude of $P = +0.86$ mag.

Integrated Color. Measurements of the integrated color of the LMC give it a color of $B - V = +0.3$, indicating that the Large Magellanic Cloud is very blue, typical of its type. Its color reflects the large number of very luminous hot stars found in the LMC.

Distribution of Light. Studies of the distribution of surface brightness of the Large Magellanic Cloud have been greatly hampered by the difficulties inherent in measuring a large area with an uneven foreground. Foreground stars in our galaxy contribute to the measured integrated light and must in some way be subtracted from the final result. In the brightest parts of the LMC the surface brightness is the equivalent of $B = 21.3$ mag/(sec of arc)^2 and $V = 21.0$ mag/(sec of arc)^2. Studies from small-scale photographs show that the isophotes of the LMC are very irregular in the center but become more nearly circular in the outer regions. The photoelectric observations of Elsasser are reproduced in Figure 6.1, where this structure is shown very clearly.

Distribution of Color. The variation of color across the galaxy is correlated to some degree with the variation of surface brightness, as would be expected if the surface brightness is influenced primarily by the stellar composition. The color is on the average rather uniform over the Cloud with small variations occurring, especially in the regions of bright stellar associations. The color ranges between values of $B - V$ of 0.5 and 0.1 with a tendency for the galaxy to be reddest in its southern portions. Figure 6.1 reproduces Elsasser's photoelectrically determined isochromes.

Dimensions. Estimates of the mean diameter of the Large Magellanic Cloud vary over a very wide range. This quantity depends greatly upon the method of measurement and the definition of the

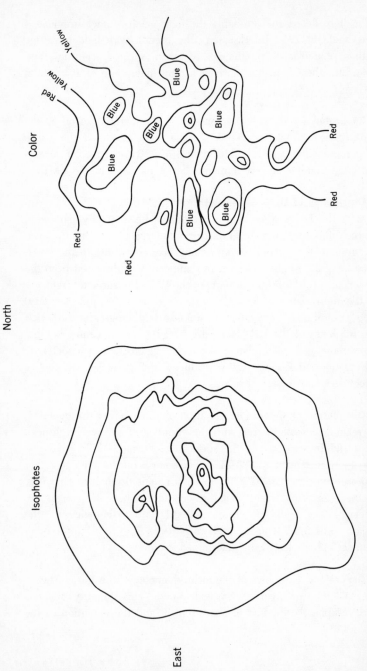

FIGURE 6.1   Isophotes and isochromes of the LMC. (After Elsasser.)

North

Color

Isophotes

East

Yellow

Red
Yellow

Red

Red

Red

Red

Blue
Blue
Blue
Blue
Blue
Blue
Blue
Blue
Blue

"boundary" of the Cloud. The dimensions of the main body of the Cloud average approximately 12 deg. However, if the neutral hydrogen of the Cloud is considered, the mean dimension becomes very much larger because of the westward extension into the area of the Small Cloud.

Distribution of Stars. Star counts show that the distribution of stars is roughly the same as the distribution of surface luminosity, with the major variations occurring in the areas where bright stars predominate. There is a very conspicuous "bar" structure at the inner part of the LMC; there are also several outer peaks, isolated from the central bar. The outermost isodents of the star counts show a roughly circular shape indicating that the very irregular central portion of the LMC is surrounded by a roughly spherical, smooth stellar envelope.

Luminosity Function. The complete integrated luminosity function for the LMC has been determined from star counts by Shapley, and it has the form

$$\log \phi \ (M) = 6.3 + 0.5 \ M$$

where $\phi \ (M)$ is the total number of stars brighter than absolute magnitude M. This relation applies to the apparent magnitude interval of $m_{pg} = 9.0$–17.0. This luminosity function is roughly similar to that of other irregular galaxies and is typical of the luminosity function of population I stars. A redetermination of the exact form of the luminosity function using modern photometric techniques has not been carried out and is something that is currently needed.

Neutral Hydrogen Content. From 21-cm studies of the content of neutral hydrogen in the LMC it has been found that the H I component of the Cloud is roughly 1.7 times larger than the size of the Cloud determined by Elsasser's photometry. This does not include the extension of the feeble H I radiation toward the Small Cloud. The total mass of neutral hydrogen is approximately 3×10^9 solar masses, leading to a very small ratio of mass to luminosity. A small M/L ratio is typical of irregular galaxies.

A summary of the integrated properties of the Large Magellanic Cloud is given in Table 6.1.

TABLE 6.1   INTEGRATED PROPERTIES OF THE LMC

QUANTITY	PROBABLE VALUE
Magnitude (V)	+1.2
Color (B — V)	+0.3
Mean diameter	~12°
Mass	~2 × 10^{10} M_⊙
Mass of H I	~3 × 10^9 M_⊙
Distance	~50 kpc

STELLAR CONTENT

Early studies of the content of the Magellanic Clouds, primarily those under the direction of Shapley of Harvard, concentrated on peculiar stars such as variable stars, exceedingly red stars, and stars with peculiar spectra. Table 6.2 summarizes the various types of stars that have been found in the Large Magellanic Cloud and gives the available data on their properties.

TABLE 6.2   TYPES OF STARS DETECTED IN THE LMC

TYPE	PROPERTIES
O-B stars	$V \geqslant 10, B - V \sim -0.2$
Supergiants	$V \geqslant 10, B - V \sim 1.8$
Giants	$V \geqslant 16, +0.6 < B - V < +2.0$
Classical cepheids	$11 < V < 18, 1^d < P < 100^d$
RR Lyrae variables	$V \approx 19.2$
Eclipsing variables	Very abundant at all magnitudes
Population II cepheids	Abnormally bright
Irregular red variables	Abundant
Semiregular red variables	Abundant
β Canis Majoris stars	Bright
Novae	$V \approx 12$ at maximum
Wolf-Rayet stars	Bright

Field stars of the Large Magellanic Cloud have been studied by means of both spectroscopy and multicolor photometry. For stars brighter than about 12th magnitude, spectra have been obtained which allow an easy separation of foreground stars in our Galaxy from true members of the Cloud by radial velocities. Figure 6.2

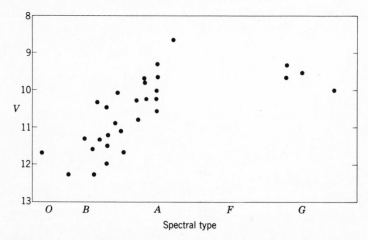

FIGURE 6.2   Hertzsprung-Russell diagram for the brightest stars in the LMC. (After Feast, Thackeray, and Wesselink.)

shows a Hertzsprung-Russell diagram for 30 LMC stars identified by this means. This H-R diagram was the first to be obtained for an entire galaxy and is exceedingly important to the problem of the development and evolution of stars of large mass. The diagram shows a very decided turnoff from the main sequence in the direction toward cooler stars at high luminosities, proving that the most massive stars must spend only a small fraction of their lifetime as hot main sequence stars and are more easily caught in a more advanced stage of evolution, either as supergiant A or B stars or as supergiant cool G and K stars.

UBV photometry of field stars in the Magellanic Clouds has been carried out in several regions. Because of the great difficulty of carrying out accurate photometry in the very crowded regions of the LMC near its bar, the photometry that has been published is primarily for fields in fairly open portions. An example of such a color-magnitude diagram is given in Figure 6.3 where the meas-

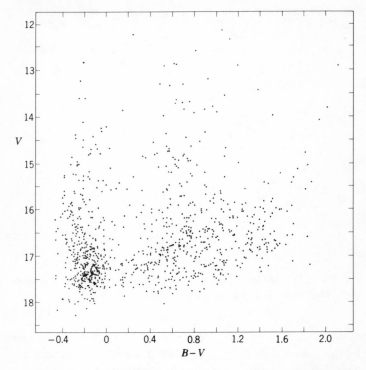

FIGURE 6.3   Color-magnitude diagram for a portion of the LMC.

urements for 1,000 field stars are presented. This diagram shows that the field has a conspicuous main sequence, which agrees accurately in position with the age-zero main sequence found for our Galaxy. It also is very conspicuously rich in giant stars with absolute magnitudes of about 0 to −3, stars of a type also common in our Galaxy. Probably the majority of stars of intermediate color shown in Figure 6.3 are foreground stars. The conclusions drawn from study of the field stars of the LMC are that the stars are very similar to stars in the solar neighborhood of our Galaxy, that there is a rich population of young unevolved stars, and that there are large numbers of old, evolved giant stars. Figure 6.4 shows the

luminosity function plotted from the measurements of field stars
given in Figure 6.3 and compares this luminosity function with
that for the solar neighborhood. Here the only conspicuous differ-

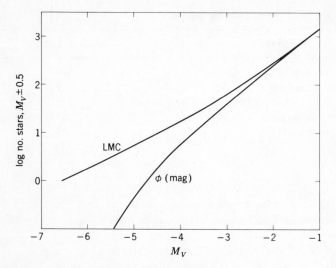

FIGURE 6.4   A comparison of the luminosity function of the solar neighborhood [$\phi(m)$] with that for a region in the LMC.

ence between the two areas is shown to be the comparative rich-
ness of the LMC in very luminous young stars.

Variable Stars. In the early part of this century Henrietta Leavitt,
at Harvard, discovered and studied hundreds of variable stars in
the Magellanic Clouds. Harlow Shapley and his assistants continued
Miss Leavitt's work on them so that now the total number of variables in the LMC exceeds 2,000. By far the majority of these
variables are classical cepheids, though only approximately 600
cepheids have been studied sufficiently to be definitely identified
as such. Estimates based on recent thorough searches in small areas
indicate that approximately one-half of all the variable stars belonging to the LMC have been discovered so far. The total number
of cepheids in the LMC is probably 3,000, with a further 1,000

62

variable stars of other types. Table 6.3 lists the present status of the discovery of various types of variables.

TABLE 6.3   VARIABLES IN THE LMC

TYPE	NUMBER KNOWN
Classical cepheids	590
Type II cepheids	7
Irregular and semiregular red and long period	110
RR Lyrae variables	21
Undetermined	1,420
Total	2,148

In addition to Shapley's many papers dealing with the light curves of the LMC cepheids, there have been several recent studies

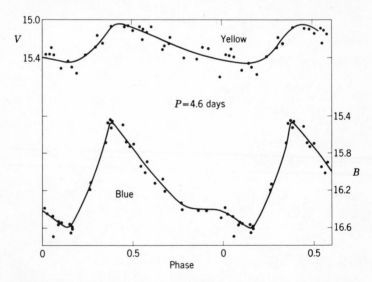

FIGURE 6.5   Example of a light curve, measured in two colors, of a cepheid (HV 12974) in the LMC.

based on photoelectric measurements. Figure 6.5 shows an example of a LMC cepheid measured in two colors, and Figure 6.6 presents

a period-luminosity diagram found for a region of the LMC. The
shape of the period-luminosity relationship has been found to be

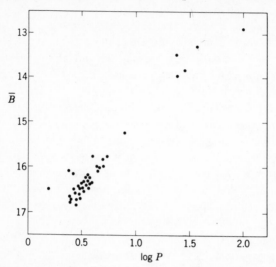

FIGURE 6.6   Period-luminosity diagram of some LMC cepheids measured by Sandage and his collaborators.

fairly constant over the Cloud, as far as tests have been carried out,
and has the following form:

$$\overline{B} = 18.2 - 2.8 \log P$$

where $\overline{B}$ is the mean luminosity measured in the blue and P is the
period in days. This period-luminosity relationship seems to be
rather similar to that for our Galaxy and for the galaxy M 31, but
it is not exactly the same as that derived for the SMC or for other
small galaxies in the local group. Further photometry of individual
stars done directly with a photoelectric photometer may clear up
this discrepancy. If the discrepancy is real, however, then the
cepheids are not very reliable distance indicators for these galaxies.

There are 23 long period variables in the direction of the LMC,
but it is not yet known whether these stars are members of the
Cloud or foreground objects in our Galaxy.

Of the large numbers of irregular variables found in the LMC, there seem to be two types, those which are yellow and vary cyclically and those which are red and vary irregularly. Neither type has been studied in great detail in the LMC so far.

Most of the eclipsing variable stars found in the Magellanic Clouds have short periods and are of the β Lyrae type. The statistics indicate that the search for eclipsing variables is far from complete in the LMC but that they are probably approximately as common as they are in our Galaxy.

The five novae found so far in the LMC have been the subject of several studies. The mean absolute magnitudes at maximum for these objects turn out to be very close to that derived for our own Galaxy. All have reached apparent magnitudes between $m_{pg} = 13$ and $m_{pg} = 11$, leading to a range in absolute magnitude of $M_{pg} = -5.6$ to $M_{pg} = -7.6$. In all cases the pre-nova star was below the threshold of the plates, which is approximately 18th magnitude.

Star Clusters. It was realized that the Magellanic Clouds were rich in star clusters by the very first astronomers to point telescopes at them. Today the total number of known clusters of stars in the LMC has reached a value of nearly 1,600. By far the majority of these are small, open clusters similar to the galactic clusters of the Milky Way, but approximately 60 clusters are different from this, being very luminous and rich.

The Red Globular Clusters. Thirty-five clusters in the LMC have been found (from their color-magnitude diagrams) to be red globular clusters like the globular clusters of our Galaxy. These range from exceedingly luminous, very rich clusters to those which are barely recognizable as globular clusters. They seem to have color-magnitude diagrams that are fairly similar to those of globulars in our Galaxy. There are, however, a few indications that the majority of the globular clusters of the LMC are more like the nuclear globular clusters of our Galaxy than like the halo globular clusters; that is, they tend to have more gently sloping giant branches, indicating a moderate heavy-element abundance (Figure 6.7). A few clusters, however, are very like the extreme metal-poor clusters of the Galactic halo, and these clusters contain RR Lyrae variables.

Blue Globular Clusters. The more puzzling type of clusters found in the LMC are the so-called "blue globular clusters." These clus-

ters look like normal globular clusters. They are large, circular in
outline, and heavily populated with stars. However, their integrated

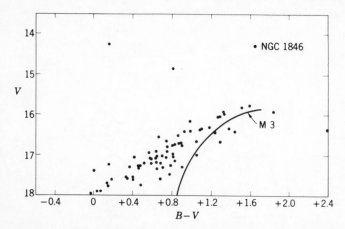

FIGURE 6.7   Color-magnitude diagram of the LMC globular cluster
NGC 1846, compared with that for M 3 (in our Galaxy).

spectral types are early A or F, and their integrated colors are
blue, much bluer than normal globular cluster colors. Color-magnitude diagrams of these clusters show them to be rather similar to
open clusters of the Cloud but with very much larger numbers of
stars. The blue globular clusters that have been measured range in
age from 10^6 years to 10^9 years. In chemical composition they apparently differ from open clusters in our Galaxy, as the red giant
members of the clusters are too luminous by comparison. This can
be explained on the basis of a somewhat depleted heavy-element
abundance, leading to a smaller opacity of the atmosphere of the
star because of fewer electrons. There is still a great deal of research
to be carried out on these clusters. Only a few have been studied in
detail, and these few have been the subject of some controversy.
Figure 6.8 shows an example of a color-magnitude diagram for
NGC 1831, one of the most luminous and rich blue globular clusters. It is compared with galactic clusters and globular clusters of
our Galaxy in Figure 6.8, where it is obvious that NGC 1831 seems

to be younger than globular clusters in our Galaxy, because of the much brighter main sequence turnoff, but different from clusters of our Galaxy of comparable age. This difference is probably the chemical composition difference mentioned above.

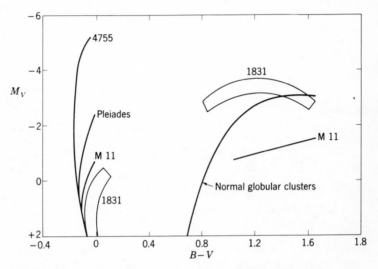

FIGURE 6.8   A comparison of the color-magnitude diagram of an LMC "blue globular cluster," NGC 1831, with clusters of our Galaxy.

Open Clusters. There are approximately 1,540 clusters in the Large Magellanic Cloud that have been identified as open clusters similar to the clusters in the plane of the Milky Way. Color-magnitude diagrams for several of these are shown schematically in Figure 6.9. Here it is seen that the open clusters of the Large Magellanic Cloud are rather similar to those in our Galaxy both in number of stars and in color-magnitude array. There is some indication that the chemical composition, at least in the mean, is not exactly the same, however. It is probably true that chemical differences are small.

Gas Content. The LMC contains some 400 emission nebulosities, most of which were discovered in early visual surveys of the Cloud. The largest and by far the most thoroughly studied of these is the object called 30 Doradus, one of the largest emission nebulosities known. Its diameter is roughly 500 parsecs, and its total mass has been estimated to be 5×10^6 solar masses. In its nucleus instead

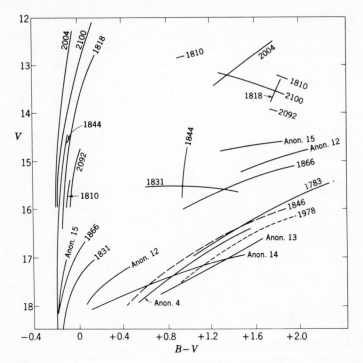

FIGURE 6.9   Composite color-magnitude diagram of LMC clusters of various types.

of a single exciting star it contains an entire rich cluster of super-luminous O- and B-type stars.

Among the other emission nebulosities of the LMC are many very small ones, including some unresolved objects. Most of the latter are believed to be simply small, unresolved H II regions, but a few are now known to be planetary nebulae. The H II regions are concentrated in areas where the luminous star density is high, but the planetary nebulae are distributed more or less uniformly over the entire field of the galaxy.

The 21-cm measures in the LMC show that it is exceedingly rich in neutral hydrogen. Recent very complete studies with the 210-ft radio telescope in Australia have shown that the distribution of H I is exceedingly patchy and clumpy with large concentrations in several individual clouds. A weak general background extends over the entire galaxy and forms a connecting arm extending toward the Small Magellanic Cloud. The range in velocity of the neutral hydrogen is from +240 to +310 km/sec (with respect to the sun), and this range has been used to obtain an estimate of the mass of the LMC by interpreting the radial velocity measures in terms of rotation of the Cloud. Figure 6.10 gives the distribution of neutral

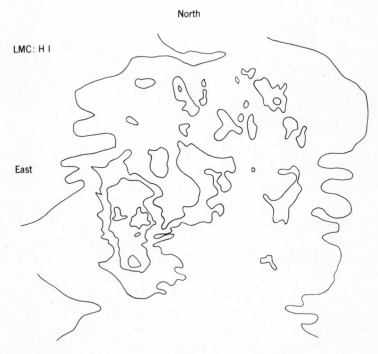

FIGURE 6.10   Isodensity plot showing neutral hydrogen concentrations in the LMC. (After McGee.)

hydrogen in the Large Magellanic Cloud measured by McGee, showing that the conspicuous bar of the cloud that is so obvious in visual photographs barely shows at all in the neutral hydrogen, indicating that this bar is primarily an old feature with no component of uncondensed stellar material.

Studies of the radio radiation from sources of continuum radio emission in the LMC show excellent agreement in location with optical H II regions. Also there are certain similarities between the location of H I and the continuum sources; certain areas that are very rich in H I are also intense in the continuum. This is striking evidence for the hypothesis that stellar formation is going on in the LCM in locations near the centers of large neutral hydrogen masses where the density is large enough that condensation into stars and H II regions is possible. Approximately one hundred times as much mass in such regions is observed in H I as is observed in H II, even for those very rich in O- and B-type stars.

Dust Content. There has been a remarkably small amount of dust observed in the LMC, considering its high gas content. Shapley has pointed out that galaxies are visible through the Cloud up to fairly close to the central regions. The best estimate as to how much dust is there comes from measurements of interstellar reddening and of interstellar lines. The reddening within the Cloud can be estimated from the color-magnitude diagrams of clusters and from UBV measures of O- and B-type stars in the Clouds. These measures all indicate a rather small amount of reddening, perhaps color excesses of less than 0.1 mag, indicating a total absorption of dust in front of the stars measured of less than 0.3 mag. This is very much smaller than the amount of reddening found within an arm of our Galaxy or of M 31. There is still a considerable amount of uncertainty about the results from the three-color observations, so that the above-quoted results should be looked upon as very preliminary. The fact that galaxies are not observed through the main body of the Cloud indicates that there certainly must be a great deal more absorption deep in the Cloud than the measurements of the brightest O and B stars indicate. The measures of interstellar lines suggest that the amount of gas in the areas where measurements were made is approximately the same as in the neighborhood of the sun.

The distance to the LMC may be determined from several sources of data, the most accurate being the period-luminosity relation for classical cepheids and the apparent magnitudes of RR Lyrae variables. From the equation on page 63 and the period-luminosity relation for our Galaxy, a distance of 53 kpc is inferred. No photoelectric measurements of RR Lyrae variables in the LMC have yet been obtained, but from less reliable data on their brightness a distance of about 50 kpc is implied, so that this figure is no doubt approximately correct.

THE SMALL MAGELLANIC CLOUD

The physical size and contents of the Small Magellanic Cloud are smaller in number than for the LMC, but the Small Cloud's shape and population are not very different. In structure it resembles a crude half-circle, with most of the bright, young stars concentrated at one side. The H I structure is very complicated, at least two components with different velocities having been discovered. Recent radio and optical evidence suggests that these two objects are receding from each other with a velocity (line-of-sight component) of about 30 km/sec.

The galaxy has in addition a "wing" at some distance from the main body that contains only young stars and long period cepheid variables. The SMC is a complex object that will reward the intense study that is planned for it. Because of its many similarities to the LMC, it will not be discussed here in more detail.

the
local group
of
galaxies

The concept of a local group of galaxies originated with the discovery that certain conspicuous ones, such as M 31, were much closer than the general background of nearby galaxies—that in fact these close galaxies formed a rather dense clump in a relatively less dense field. Recent research has substantiated this concept. However, because dwarf elliptical galaxies such as the Ursa Minor Dwarf are very difficult to detect at distances beyond about 300 kpc, it is not yet clear whether local clustering is as pronounced for them as for the more luminous objects.

As Figure 7.1 shows, the local group is somewhat flattened in shape and is primarily concentrated in the south galactic hemisphere, with our Galaxy near one edge. Its diameter is roughly 800

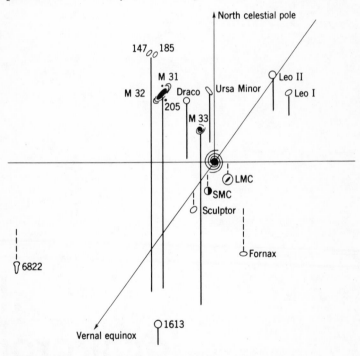

FIGURE 7.1   Three-dimensional schematic diagram of the local group. Galaxy images are not to scale.

kpc, and its thickness is about half of this value. The nearest conspicuous outsiders are about 1,100 kpc distant, and numerous other bright spirals are within 1,500 kpc. The region in between the boundary of the local group and these objects is probably devoid of luminous spiral galaxies, but it may contain several faint irregulars or elliptical galaxies.

As defined by these boundaries, the local group consists of 28 objects, 17 of which are generally considered true galaxies, and 11 of which are "intergalactic tramp" globular clusters. Of the galaxies, only three are spirals, while 4 are irregulars, and 10 are ellipticals. Table 7.1 summarizes the properties of each.

The general information that can be obtained from a study of the local group is considerable. For instance, it is the source of the fundamental calibrations of extragalactic distance scales (Chapter 12). The radial velocities of local-group galaxies have been used to obtain a value for the "solar motion" (the apparent velocity of the Sun) that gives a value for the rate of rotation of our Galaxy at the position of the Sun. The study of the content of these galaxies, all of which can be resolved into stars and studied photometrically, is valuable to problems of stellar evolution and stellar structure. The detailed study of the forms and structures of these nearby objects allows progress to be made in the inquiry into the mode of evolution of galaxies. The density of galaxies in space also can be studied; only in the local group can we hope to observe all of the numerous subluminous systems that appear to populate space so generously. Since we are able to find the fainter members of the local group, it is the best source of information for the luminosity function of galaxies.

In the following paragraphs each member of the local group will be discussed in detail, its known properties summarized, and its importance to other extragalactic problems pointed out. The galaxies will be given in order of their right ascension.

MEMBERS OF THE LOCAL GROUP

NGC 147. A faint and distant companion to the galaxy M 31, NGC 147 has the color and structure of a normal elliptical galaxy. Its luminosity gradient is exceedingly gentle, making it an inconspicuous object. It is attended by certainly two and possibly four

TABLE 7.1 THE LOCAL GROUP OF GALAXIES

NAME	TYPE	α	δ, deg	b, deg	DIAM., min	DIAM., kpc	DIST., kpc	m-M	m	M	NO. OF GLOBULAR CLUSTERS	MASS $M_\odot$	V_0, km/sec
Galaxy	S	—	—	—	—	—	10.5	—	—	—	~120	2×10^{11}	—
NGC 147	E4	$0^h 30.4^m$	48.2	−14	12	2.4	680	24.1	10.5	−13.6	4?	?	—
NGC 185	E2	0 36.1	48.1	−14	16	2.9	680	24.1	10.2	−13.9	4?	?	−270
NGC 205	E5	0 37.6	41.4	−21	16	4.2	680	24.2	8.9	−15.7	8	?	−239
M 31	Sb	0 40.0	41.1	−20	210	52	680	24.2	4.6	−20.0	~300	4×10^{11}	−267
M 32	E2	0 40.0	40.6	−22	8	2.1	680	24.2	9.1	−15.5	?	2×10^{9}	−220
SMC	Irr I	0 50.0	−73.0	−45	320	5	60	18.8	2.4	−16.2	?	?	+168
Sculptor	E3	0 57.5	−34.0	−83	106	2.4	86	19.7	9.8	−9.9	0	3×10^{6}	—
IC 1613	Irr I	1 00.6	1.7	−60	20	4	680	24.1	10.0	−14.1	0	?	−235
M 33	Sc	1 31.1	30.4	−31	70	18	700	24.3	6.6	−18.1	?	2×10^{10}	−190
Fornax	E3	2 37.5	−34.7	−64	100	6.2	188	21.4	9	−12.4	5	2×10^{7}	−73
LMC	Irr I	5 26.0	−69.0	−33	550	8	53	18.6	1.0	−17.6	35	?	+276
Leo I	E3	10 5.8	12.6	+50	28	1.8	230	21.8	11.3	−10.5	0	3×10^{6}	—
Leo II	E0	11 10.8	22.4	+69	20	1.3	230	21.8	12.8	−9.0	0	10^{6}	—
Ursa Minor	E6	15 8.2	67.3	+45	60	2.4	68	19.1	—	—	0	10^{5}	—
Draco	E3	17 19.4	58.0	+34	52	1.0	77	19.4	—	—	0	10^{5}	—
NGC 6822	Irr I	19 42.1	−14.9	−20	20	1.7	660	24.0	9.5	−14.5	?	?	−34

globular clusters, the color of which is indicative that they are normal globular clusters similar to the halo clusters of our Galaxy. NGC 147 contains no absorbing dust, and galaxies are visible through it right up to the central regions. Unlike its companion, NGC 185, the galaxy contains no B stars in its center, the brightest stars being red giants at apparent magnitude of approximately $M_B \approx 21$.

NGC 185. This companion galaxy to NGC 147 is also a distant companion to the spiral galaxy M 31. It has a steeper density gradient than NGC 147 and is therefore a more conspicuous object. The center of NGC 185 is unusual in that it contains two dark absorbing patches, very similar in size and density to those found in the Milky Way. They have mean dimensions of 25 parsecs and 45 parsecs and estimated masses of 20 and 150 solar masses, respectively. Baade discovered approximately 12 bright B stars in the center of NGC 185. These stars have apparent magnitudes in the blue of about 20, giving them absolute magnitudes of about -4. Recent computations have shown that if this is indicative that there is a small population I component in the center of NGC 185, the total mass of such a component must be on the order of 2×10^5 solar masses. Estimates based on this and also on the total mass of dust in NGC 185 have led to a prediction that it contains approximately 4×10^4 solar masses of hydrogen gas. Baade has also discovered a few long-period variable stars, but these have not yet been studied.

NGC 205. One of the two very close companions to M 31, NGC 205 is a highly elongated elliptical galaxy that is in most respects very similar to NGC 185. It has two conspicuous absorption patches due to dust near its center; it has a moderate luminosity gradient; it has 10 or so bright B stars in its central regions; and it has a few long period variable stars. It has more globular clusters than NGC 185, eight in number, and is 2 mag more luminous. Its proximity to M 31 causes tidal distortions of its outer parts, discernible in the outer isophotes of the galaxy.

One of the most interesting studies of NGC 205 was that of

Baum and Schwarzschild, who compared the surface brightness with the star count to a particular magnitude and found from this that the stellar population in NGC 205 must be very nearly the same as in a halo globular cluster; that is, NGC 205 must contain low-metal-abundance population II stars.

M 31. The giant spiral galaxy M 31 (NGC 224) is of such importance to so many problems that a discussion of it will be given in a separate chapter (Chapter 8).

M 32. The small elliptical companion of M 31, M 32 (NGC 221), has been the subject of several studies. It has a high luminosity gradient and a very bright central intensity. Its total mass has been estimated by the means of velocity dispersion measurements (see Chapter 5). The observed radial velocity dispersion is 138 km/sec, and under the usual assumptions this means a total mass of about 2×10^9 solar masses. Thus, the mass-light ratio (photographic) is about 13. Of course, there are many assumptions involved in calculating these quantities, as pointed out in Chapter 5.

The stellar population and chemical composition of M 32 can be deduced in principle from a combination of a study of its spectrum and its derived mass-light ratio. The integrated light from the spectrum is very similar to that of normal giants of types G8 III to K III. In the ultraviolet, photoelectric scans indicate an enrichment over the ultraviolet intensity of a G8 III standard, which may indicate the presence of late F- or early G-type main sequence stars.

A recent attempt to detect neutral hydrogen in M 32 produced a negative result, leading to an upper limit on the mass of neutral atomic hydrogen of 2.5×10^7 solar masses. Therefore the ratio of the mass of H I to the total mass is very small, less than 0.007.

There have been several studies of the interaction between M 32 and the giant spiral M 31. In one of these, Schwarzschild deduced from an apparent asymmetry in the rotation curve of M 31 that the mass of M32 must be on the order of 2.5×10^{10} solar masses. This value is greater than that described in the paragraphs above, a possible consequence of the uncertainty in the assumptions that Schwarzschild had to make. More recently, Arp has suggested that the irregularity in the spiral pattern of M 31 may be the consequence of a deformation produced on M 31 by the presence of M 32. This also seems to show up as a peculiar effect noticeable on 21-cm radio observations. The gas arms and star arms agree in position on the north side of M 31, but on the south side, near M 32, the gas arms are displaced 1 or 2 kpc from the star arms. Arp believes that this may be partially or wholly caused by plasma magnetic effects.

The Small Magellanic Cloud. The Magellanic Clouds have already been discussed in Chapter 6, where their properties and their importance were summarized.

Sculptor. As an example of a nearby elliptical galaxy that can be studied in detail, the Sculptor galaxy is discussed at length in Chapter 9.

IC 1613. This irregular galaxy was studied for many, many years by the Mt. Wilson astronomer, Walter Baade. He found it to be rather similar in many ways to the Magellanic Clouds, though much smaller and much less complex. Besides an ill-defined bar in the center, IC 1613 contains two groups of very blue stars, one much brighter than the other. The more conspicuous stellar association contains the brightest star in the system, of apparent mag 17.0 (photographic), and the longest period cepheid, as well as several emission regions of various intensities and sizes, the largest of which is 143 parsecs in diameter. It is in this area that star formation seems to be going on at the present time as it is here that the most luminous stars and the most gas and dust are found.

Baade discovered 63 variables in all in the galaxy, 36 of which have been studied in detail. Twenty-five of these variables are cepheids, with periods ranging from 2.4 to 146 days. They form a period-luminosity relationship, used by Baade to calculate a distance for the system of 680 parsecs. There is still some question, however, about the agreement of the slope of the period-luminosity relationship with that for our Galaxy or the Magellanic Clouds. Seven of the variable stars are irregular; six of these are red stars with absolute magnitudes concentrated around the value of −4.4 mag, with none very much brighter or fainter than this. The seventh irregular variable is a very blue star with a mean absolute magnitude of −4. It seemed to Baade to be similar to the bright blue stars found by Hubble and Sandage in M 31 and M 33, though very much fainter. Baade also found one long period variable star with a period of 446 days, an absolute magnitude of −5 (photographic), and an amplitude of 1.8 mag. A normal eclipsing binary, a nova, not seen at maximum, and one strange unexplained variable star with a period of 29 days complete Baade's list.

IC 1613 was found to have an underlying large subsystem of old population II stars covering an area of 25 min by 20 min, roughly elliptical in shape. This contrasts with the patchy and ragged smaller area of population I stars and indicates that the star formation that is going on at the present time is only the most recent activity of this sort in a very long history of a very old galaxy (see Chapter 11).

M 33. The small spiral galaxy M 33 (NGC 598) is discussed in detail along with M 31 in Chapter 8.

Fornax. Because of its historical importance, the Fornax system is discussed separately (Chapter 9).

The Large Magellanic Cloud. Discussed previously (Chapter 6), the Large Magellanic Cloud is one of the most important members of the group because of its complexity, proximity, and diversity.

Leo I. The two most distant known dwarf elliptical galaxies in the local group are the Leo systems discovered in 1950 by Harrington and Wilson. Leo I has not been extensively studied because of its proximity to the star Regulus which makes photography very difficult for large telescopes with correcting lenses. A few RR Lyrae variables were found by Baade and more have recently been found by others, but periods and light curves for these have not yet been obtained. There are no globular clusters and no evidence for dust or gas in the system. A diffuse object near the major axis of Leo I may be a part of the system, but it has the appearance on the best plates of a distant spiral galaxy, and therefore is probably unrelated to the system.

The distribution of stars in Leo I has been determined from star counts which show that it is a perfectly symmetrical elliptical galaxy with a ratio of axes of 0.69. The star density profile resem-

bles those of Sculptor and Fornax, showing distinctly a sharp cutoff radius which, in the case of the Leo I system, corresponds to a
linear radius of 0.95 kpc.

Leo II. At about the same distance as the Leo I system, Leo II
similarly has its brightest stars at approximately $m_{pg} = 20.0$. Baade
discovered that the system is rich in cluster-type variables, but none
of these has yet been studied. There are no globular clusters or no
obvious nebulae, and the system seems to be quite transparent, distant galaxies being visible through it right up to its center. Star
counts show that it is essentially perfectly circular in outline. The
projected density of counted stars looks very much like that for
Leo I and the Sculptor and Fornax systems. There is a sharp cutoff
radius at a distance from the center of 12 min of arc, which is
equivalent to 0.80 kpc. This size, like that for Leo I, is somewhat
smaller than the predicted current gravitational cutoff.

Draco. The Draco dwarf galaxy was discovered in 1955 by Wilson
and was extensively studied by Baade and Miss Swope. These astronomers have measured the color-magnitude diagram of the system (Figure 7.2) and have studied its variable star population in
great detail. They discovered that Draco contains many RR Lyrae
variables, all of a normal type except for four which have unusally
long periods (greater than a day) and are abnormally bright. Figure 7.3 shows their results in terms of a period-magnitude diagram.
The mean period of the variables is 0.54 days. Baade and Swope
found that the magnitude of the RR Lyrae variable stars at mean
luminosity is 20.48 in B, indicating an apparent distance modulus
for the system of 19.58. If a correction for galactic absorption is
applied, the true distance modulus is reduced to approximately
19.4, indicating that the linear distance to Draco is only 68 kpc.
Draco contains no globular clusters or obvious nebulae. Galaxies are
conspicuous right up to the center of the system, indicating that it
contains little or no dust. Its total magnitude has not yet been
measured.

Star counts have shown that the system is perfectly elliptical with
an ellipticity of 0.29 (the ratio of axes is 0.71). The projected

density profile looks very much like that of the other elliptical galaxies in the local group, and a cutoff radius is detected at a

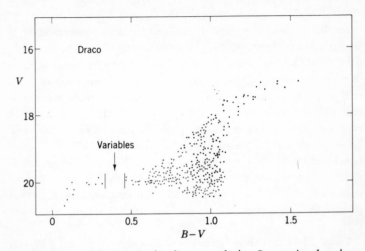

FIGURE 7.2   Color-magnitude diagram of the Draco dwarf galaxy. (After Baade and Swope.)

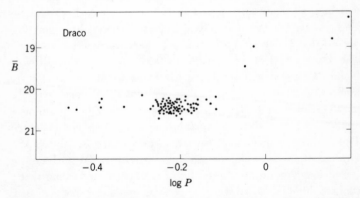

FIGURE 7.3   Period-luminosity relation for RR Lyrae variables in Draco. (After Baade and Swope.)

distance of 26 min of arc, corresponding to a linear radius of 0.51 kpc, in very good agreement with the predicted tidal limit to the system.

The mass of the Draco system can be estimated from the luminosity function determined by Baade and Swope, which is nearly identical to that of M 3 in shape. The comparison shows that Draco is less massive than the globular cluster M 3 with a mass ratio for Draco/M 3 of 0.87. This leads to a total mass for Draco of approximately 10^5 solar masses. Draco therefore is intrinsically the smallest galaxy in the local group, and the least massive.

Ursa Minor. The Ursa Minor dwarf elliptical galaxy was discovered on the original plates of the Palomar sky survey in about 1950. Baade obtained an excellent series of plates of the system with the 200-in. telescope at Palomar, and his plates have been used by Van Agt to obtain a color-magnitude diagram and to carry out a photometric study of the RR Lyrae variable star population. The total system contains approximately 90 variable stars of this type, which have a magnitude at mean luminosity of approximately $B = 20.3$. The true distance modulus as computed for Draco is approximately 19.1, corresponding to a linear distance of a little less than that of Draco. The system contains no globular clusters, no emission nebulae, and no dust that can be detected. Its stars are arranged in a symmetrical, highly elliptical form with an ellipticity of 0.55. The density profile is similar to that for other dwarf elliptical galaxies. The radius is very difficult to determine from star counts but has been estimated to be approximately 1.2 kpc, with a large uncertainty. The total mass of the system can be estimated in much the same way as for Draco, by comparison of luminosity functions, and it is found by these means that the Ursa Minor system is slightly more massive than the globular cluster M 3, with a ratio of masses of 1.1. Thus the total mass of the system must be approximately 1.5×10^5 solar masses.

POSSIBLE MEMBERS

In addition to the galaxies listed above, there are several others that may be members of the local group, but for which membership has not yet been thoroughly investigated. These include four small irregular galaxies and two fairly large spirals. Most of these are probably just beyond the limits of the group, but accurate distances have not been determined for them, either because they are too small and poor in stars or because they are behind a large and unknown amount of absorbing dust in the Milky Way. Table 7.2 summarizes available data on them.

TABLE 7.2   POSSIBLE MEMBERS OF THE LOCAL GROUP

NAME	TYPE	DIAMETER, min of arc	COMMENTS
IGC 2427	Sc	5	Suggested by Shapley
IC 10	Irr I	15	Probably too distant ($\sim$1.5 Mpc)
IC 342	Sc	20	Highly obscured
WLM	Irr I	13	Elongated
Leo A	Irr I	—	Elongated, discovered by Zwicky
Sextans	Irr I	5	Square-shaped object, discovered by Zwicky

The irregular galaxies Sextans and Leo A were discovered by Zwicky with the 18-in. Schmidt on Palomar in about 1940. Both are apparently very small and uncomplicated objects, with a smattering of young stars scattered over a smooth, unresolved background. The Sextans system, like IC 10, is remarkable in shape, appearing nearly square in outline. Neutral hydrogen has been detected in IC 10, and its total mass in the form of gas is 2×10^8 solar masses. The WLM galaxy was named for the astronomers Wolf, Lundmark, and Mellotte. It is elliptical in outline, with a reddish integrated color, indicating a fairly rich population of old stars, though young stars are also conspicuous.

The two spiral galaxies listed in Table 7.2 are very close to the plane of the Milky Way and may suffer several magnitudes of absorption. They have not been studied in detail.

INTERGALACTIC GLOBULAR CLUSTERS

The Palomar sky survey turned up five new globular clusters at great distances, and studies of some of these showed that they are

TABLE 7.3   INTERGALACTIC GLOBULAR CLUSTERS

NAME	DIAMETER	MAGNITUDE OF BRIGHTEST STARS	PROBABLE DISTANCE, kpc
Palomar 1	1.3	19	
Palomar 3	2.2	20.0	130
Palomar 4	2.5	19.9	120
Palomar 12	2.1	17	75
Capricorn (Zwicky)	10	17	80

definitely beyond the usually accepted boundaries of our Galaxy. It is not clear whether they should be called clusters or galaxies, but so far most astronomers have adopted the term intergalactic globular clusters, or intergalactic "tramps." Table 7.3 lists their characteristics. They are all abnormally large for their total mass, a probable result of their great distance from the tidally disturbing Galaxy.

* 8 *

M 31
and M 33

The two nearest spiral galaxies to ours are M 31 and M 33, two of the most distant members of the local group. These two objects are of great importance because they are near enough for us to obtain a detailed and precise inventory of the types of stars and interstellar matter that constitute their spiral structure. We can resolve the various population-type criteria and can measure periods of variable stars, colors of different types of stars, and the spatial distribution of various objects. These two galaxies, then, are the key to our understanding of spiral arms.

M 31

Integrated Properties. We begin our study of the "Andromeda galaxy," M 31, with a discussion of its various integrated properties. The most fundamental of the integrated properties is a total apparent magnitude. For M 31 a total magnitude is very difficult to obtain because of its large extent over the sky. No single photometric measurement with a telescope can detect the entire galaxy at one time. For that reason, what we know about its integrated magnitude is based primarily on detailed surface photometry of the galaxy, derived either photographically or photoelectrically. The three photometric studies of this sort were carried out by Holmberg, Lynga, and De Vaucouleurs, who obtained total visual apparent magnitudes for M 31 of 3.47, 3.50, and 3.58, respectively. The excellent agreement of these different determinations signifies that this is a datum that is quite accurately known today.

The total *absolute* magnitude of M 31 can be obtained by combining the values above with its measured distance. From the distance estimates discussed below, the total absolute magnitude is derived to be $M_V = -20.0$.

The total integrated color of M 31 has been measured on several occasions. The most recent determination is that by De Vaucouleurs, who found that the color in the UBV system is $B - V = +0.91$ and $U - B = +0.50$. This is fairly typical of Sb-type spirals.

The distribution of light across the image of M 31 has been measured in a number of different ways. Figure 8.1 shows a photographic scan made perpendicular to the major axis, passing near to the center. It is obvious in this scan that the spiral structure of M 31 is only a small feature of the total luminosity distribution.

The spiral arms on the nearer side are more pronounced in the scan than on the farther side, because of the absorption on the nearer side by the dust in the arms. But even on the nearer side the arms are not as conspicuous as a visual inspection of the image of the galaxy might indicate. As in other spiral galaxies, the arms seem to be merely small perturbations in the general falloff of luminosity outward from the center.

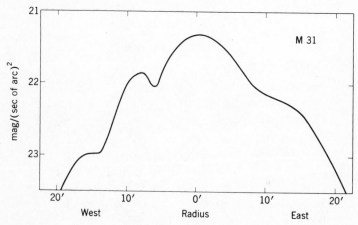

FIGURE 8.1   Profile through M 31, taken parallel to the minor axis and 10 min of arc north of it. (After Lyngå.)

Figure 8.2 shows a reproduction of isophotes optained for M 31 using a scanning technique which allows the image of the galaxy to cross the field of view of the telescope at the diurnal rate. From this photometry, De Vaucouleurs has concluded that the image of M 31 can be divided into two components, a flat one and a spheroidal one. He finds that the central amorphous bulge of M 31 results from the fact that the spheroidal component dominates the center up to a distance of about 30 min of arc. This component contributes about one-quarter of the light in the blue. The remainder of the luminosity comes from a flat disk, which includes the spiral arm structure as well as an unresolved amorphous background.

The distribution of color across the disk of M 31 has also been studied in great detail and is very informative. Figure 8.3 shows the results of a scan across the major axis. The color curves are

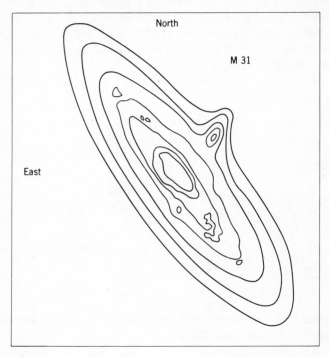

FIGURE 8.2 Isophotes of M 31, measured by direct photoelectric scanning. (After De Vaucouleurs.)

seen to be strongly related to the intensity curves, particularly in the areas near star clouds and the outer spiral arms, where the color is very blue when the intensity is high. The central color is red, indicating the predominance of old giant stars in the central bulge, but the spiral arms in the outer regions are blue, indicating the predominance there of young luminous stars.

Star counts for the entire galaxy have never been made. However, the distribution of stars in M 31 has been investigated in part by various astronomers. For instance, Van den Bergh, using the blue print of the Palomar Schmidt sky atlas, has made counts along three strips parallel to the major axis. The results potentially can be used in conjuction with the measurements of the surface

brightness and the color at each point in M 31 to obtain information about the luminosity function and color-magnitude diagram

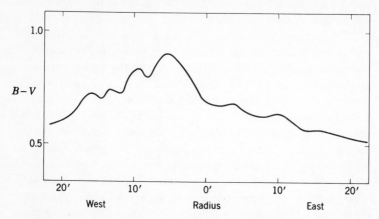

FIGURE 8.3   Color distribution along the same portion of M 31 shown
in Figure 8.1. (After Lyngå.)

of stars at that position. Such a study has not been carried out yet,
although Van den Bergh's investigation of correlations between star
density (projected) and neutral hydrogen density have given information of interest about the stellar and gaseous makeup of the
galaxy. In particular, he found that normally when the star density
was high, the neutral-hydrogen density was also high, especially in
the outer regions of the galaxy, where gas and young stars are
strongly correlated in position.

The size of M 31 is found to be very much larger than an inspection of a photograph might suggest. The major axis has a diameter
of at least 240 min of arc, to a limit of brightness of $B = 26.8$ mag/
(sec of arc)^2. Probably the galaxy actually extends even farther
than this. In linear dimensions this corresponds to a diameter of at
least 50 kpc.

The orientation of M 31 can be determined by measuring its
position angle and the ratio of the apparent axes of the disc component. The position angle of the major axis has been found to be
~37 deg, and the angle between the plane of the galaxy and the

line of sight is approximately 12 deg. There is some uncertainty in the value of the inclination angle because the true axial ratio of the galaxy is not known and must be estimated by analogy with similar galaxies seen edge-on.

The distance to M 31 has been the subject of much discussion and work. It is a quantity fundamental to our understanding of extragalactic distance criteria and is one of the prime sources of calibration of extragalactic distance indicators. The most recently determined distance, and probably the most reliable, is that obtained from the period-luminosity relationship of the cepheid variables found in the outermost arms. In these distant arms, the cepheid variables are relatively unreddened by internal absorption in M 31, and their period-luminosity relationship is well defined. The distance modulus of M 31 is estimated from the cepheid variables to be 24.17, corrected for absorption in our Galaxy. This corresponds to a linear distance of about 680 kpc. The uncertainty in this datum is about 10 percent. The novae and the globular clusters have also been used to estimate the distance of M 31, giving similar results.

The total mass of M 31 has been determined by the method of establishing a rotation curve from radial velocity measurements. This has been done both by neutral hydrogen measurements of the 21-cm velocities and by optical measurements of the emission nebulae. The results differ somewhat, according to what type of model of mass distribution is used to fit the rotation curve, but all agree that the mass is approximately 4×10^{11} solar masses. The mass of the spheroidal portion at the center of M 31 has been derived by Minkowski from the velocity dispersion in the line of sight, which is measured to be 225 km/sec, and which leads to a total mass for this portion of the galaxy of about 2×10^{11} solar masses. The mean ratio of mass to luminosity for M 31 is about 23. One percent of its total mass is detected in the form of neutral hydrogen.

Structure. The general structure of M 31 is that of a typical Sb spiral. It has a very extensive nuclear region surrounded by two spiral arms which make several circuits. There is evidence that the central portion of M 31 possesses a barred structure. The Swedish astronomers Lindblad and Lyngå have detected an east-west elongation of the core of M 31 that they interpret as a small bar structure. The spiral arms of M 31 have been studied in very great detail, primarily by the astronomer Baade, who devoted a great deal of his life to their study. Using the 200-in. telescope, Baade obtained an extensive series of plates of the arms in which he isolated the H-α emission, the ultraviolet, and the infrared areas of the spectrum. From these plates he was able to disentangle the spiral structure, which is difficult to follow because of the tilt of the galaxy. Baade found that there are two spiral arms, both originating near the nucleus of the galaxy and each winding around the center in almost two full turns. Arp has found that a logarithmic spiral of the form $r = 30$ (min of arc) $e^{0.13\phi}$, where r is the distance from the center and ϕ is the position angle, represents the spiral structure well, if distortions due to neighboring M 32 are taken into account. Baade's description of the arms as each crosses the major axis is as follows (see also Figure 8.4):

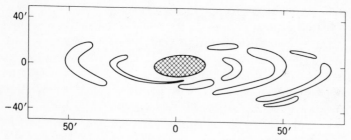

FIGURE 8.4   The arms of M 31 as plotted by Arp.

1. The first crossing of the axis is characterized by a thick and luminous arm with conspicuous dust lanes and no supergiant stars or H II regions present.
2. The second crossing of the arms is characterized by the presence of dust separating the arms and the appearance of a very few supergiant stars in the center of the arm.
3. The third crossing of the arms has much the same appearance as the second with the addition of a few H II regions.
4. The fourth crossing of the arms is characterized by a large number of supergiant stars, many H II regions, and considerably less conspicuous dust lanes.

5. The fifth crossing of the arms is characterized by a very much fainter arm made up primarily of supergiant stars and H II regions with almost no dust visible.

6. The next to the last crossing of the arms is made up of scattered groupings of supergiant stars.

7. The last visible crossing of the arms, at a distance of 20 kpc, is very inconspicuous, made up entirely of very scattered groupings of loose stellar associations.

The outer arms of M 31 are visible only on the best plates taken with the 200-in telescope, because they are very thin groupings of stars too faint to distinguish on plates of smaller scale and brighter limits. Beyond crossing 7, Baade found an association of B stars of absolute magnitude of approximately −4, 200 parsecs in diameter at a distance of about 25 kpc from the center. This is probably the most outlying stellar grouping distinguishable in M 31.

The distortion of the arms on the southern side of M 31 has been a subject of considerable investigation, primarily by Arp, who attributes this distortion to the gravitational or plasma-magnetic effects of the neighboring small galaxy M 32. Arp rectified the positions of emission nebulae found by Baade so that they appeared as we would see them if M 31 were face-on. The result was very disappointing, as the spiral structure did not immediately become obvious. The problem seemed to be a distortion of the spiral arms for half of the galaxy, and this distortion is best explained in terms of some interaction between M 31 and M 32. The exact nature of this interaction is not understood. It is not known whether it can be entirely a gravitational tidal effect or whether it may also involve magnetic fields or plasma effects.

The nucleus of M 31 has been the subject of several studies and has been found to be a very highly rotating object of small dimensions. The stars that make up this small nucleus appear to be primarily a disk population with only moderately eccentric orbits, superimposed upon the larger scale spherical population that makes up the core. The size of this small, intense nuclear area is about 100 parsecs.

Content. M 31 contains almost all recognized types of stars. It is close enough so that the largest telescopes can reach stars of absolute magnitude as faint as $M = -1$, so that all stars brighter than this limit can be detected if present. In general, the galaxy consists primarily of old, moderately metal-rich stars, which dominate the spheroidal portion of the galaxy, old metal-poor stars, which are thinly scattered over the entire galaxy and concentrated in globular clusters, and young metal-rich stars, which are located only in the outer parts of the arms.

M 31 has a well-studied population of variable stars, the cepheid variables being the most thoroughly investigated. The astronomer Baade discovered nearly 1,000 variable stars of various sorts by blinking pairs of plates covering four regions in the south part of the galaxy. Cepheids were the most commonly discovered type of star, making up as much as 70 percent of the sample, but Baade also found eclipsing variable stars, yellow irregular variable stars, long period variables, novae, and several variable stars of an undetermined type.

The cepheid variables of M 31 have light curves that are exceedingly similar to those in our Galaxy. It is therefore believed that the chemical composition and other characteristics of these variables are probably identical to those in the solar neighborhood. These cepheids are concentrated toward the arms of the galaxy, as are most bright stars. The shortest periods detected are three days, although periods shorter than that may exist below the limit of detection. Figure 8.5 shows the period-luminosity relationship derived by Baade and Swope for the cepheid variables in the outermost of the regions studied. Most of the stars shown in the diagram are normal classical-type cepheids. However, seven of them are bluer, have very different light curves, and are much less regular than normal cepheids. These seven are those that lie about a magnitude and a half fainter than the mean, and they are probably therefore population II-type cepheids. If these are neglected, the normal cepheid variables can be used to find an accurate mean period-luminosity relationship which has the form $B = 23.35 - 2.6 \log P$. This is the prime method of obtaining the distance to M 31.

The novae of M 31 have been studied in a systematic survey carried out by Arp. Of 30 novae studied he found that the rapid novae (five days was the average time that they were visible) reached an absolute magnitude of −8.5, while the slowest novae (visible for 150 days) reached an absolute magnitude of only −6.2.

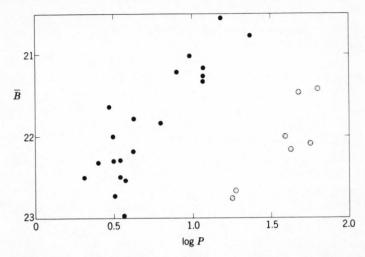

FIGURE 8.5   Period-luminosity relation for cepheids in a portion of M 31. Open circles are type II cepheids. (After Baade and Swope.)

He calculated that novae occurred at the rate of approximately 26 per year. They are useful as a check on the distance, but even more as a sample of novae of a wide variety of types that can be used to establish the properties of these objects more accurately than can be done with those of our Galaxy, the distances of which are difficult to determine.

The star clusters of M 31 have been investigated, although not in so much detail as the variable stars. Globular star clusters have been detected by both Hubble and Baade. There are approximately 300 globular clusters distributed symmetrically around the disc of M 31. The globular clusters range in absolute magnitude (in the blue) from −9.5 to about −2 or −3, the limit of the search. There appears to be a slightly different luminosity function for globular clusters for M 31 as compared to that for our Galaxy, there being more faint globular clusters in M 31 than in our Galaxy.

Open clusters are very difficult to distinguish at the distance of M 31, and no catalog of such objects has been prepared. Most of them appear simply as slightly fuzzy stellar images, and study of their detailed makeup is beyond present capabilities. Stellar associations, however, are easily recognized because of their large angular extent. A survey of stellar associations has been carried by Van den Bergh, who showed that the associations are good objects for tracing the spiral arm structure. The diameters and populations of the associations are quite similar to those found in our Galaxy near the sun.

Emission nebulae are very abundant in M 31; 700 of them have been catalogued by Baade. In the central regions all of the emission nebulae appear abnormally red, probably because of absorption by dust there. Their spectra are perfectly normal. In the outer arms they are conspicuous on the blue plates and do not seem to be highly reddened. These objects are strongly concentrated along the arms, but they are by no means limited only to the center of the spiral arms. A few even are found between arms. They are correlated in position with the presence of bright young stars and also with the presence of concentrations of neutral hydrogen, detected by the 21-cm measurements.

Planetary nebulae can be distinguished in M 31 by using appropriate filter techniques to isolate the green nebular lines, strong in planetary nebulae. Baade found several objects that he identified as planetary nebulae and measured their brightness to be somewhat brighter than absolute magnitude -2 (photographic). These objects were embedded in the rich population II portion of the galaxy, a fact expected on the basis of our identification of planetary nebulae with old population stars.

The dust content of M 31 is very considerable, although the total mass of dust in the galaxy is still only poorly known. Evidence for the existence of dust comes both from reddening of objects such as planetary nebulae and cepheid variables and from the observed polarization of globular clusters as measured by Hiltner. From polarization measurements it was found that the electric vector of the polarization is parallel to the major axis. This is very much the same situation as found for our Galaxy, where the electric vector is found to be parallel to the spiral arm structure, indicating that the particles are aligned in the direction of the spiral arms.

It has been found that M 31 is a weak source of continuum radio radiation and that this radiation comes from an extended halo or corona centered on M 31 but covering an area three times the optical size of the object. Ninety percent of the continuum radiation comes from this corona, and the remaining 10 percent comes from the area of the optical disk and probably is derived from the H II regions in the disk. The origin of the radiation from the corona is not thoroughly understood. It possibly is derived from synchrotron radiation from high-velocity charged particles which envelop M 31, but the means of their obtaining their present energies is still a matter of dispute.

M 33

The small spiral galaxy M 33 has been studied as thoroughly and as completely as M 31, but because of its smaller size and much smaller mass, the number of various types of objects found in it is smaller. Only a very small portion of the research that has been done on M 33 has been published.

Integrated Properties. The total apparent magnitude of M 33 is approximately 6.3 (B), and its total color is $B - V = +0.55$. Its color is considerably bluer than the color of M 31, as expected from the consideration that M 33 is a "later"-type spiral, richer in young stars. M 33 is only approximately 20 min of arc in radius along the major axis and nowhere has as bright a surface luminosity as in the central regions of M 31. Its color is much more uniform in distribution than for M 31, being $B - V = +0.59$ in the center and changing only to $B - V = 0.50$ in the outer regions, on the average. The diameter of M 33 is approximately 70 min of arc, which corresponds to about 18 kpc, as its distance is nearly the same as that of M 31. It is nearly face-on, much more nearly so than M 31, with an angle of inclination of 50 deg to the line of sight.

The total mass of M 33 can be measured readily by means of the radial velocities observed for H II regions and for neutral hydrogen. Both results lead to a total mass of approximately 2×10^{10} times that of the sun, so that M 33 is about one-twentieth as massive as M 31.

The nucleus of M 33 is very small, with a diameter of only a few hundred parsecs. Its spectrum is F5, indicating the presence of a mixture, probably of intermediate and old giant stars. The outer portions of M 33 are primarily made up of thick spiral arms containing many stellar associations, bright O and B stars, and emission regions. Underneath these arms in an all-enveloping sheet is a population of old red stars extending out to the limits of the spiral pattern.

Several hundred emission objects have been cataloged by Sandage and Sersic, who are using these emission objects as a calibration of the method of distance measurement by the diameter of emission objects (see Chapter 12). The spectra of several of these emission objects have been obtained, and it is found that their chemical composition is very similar to that of emission objects in our Galaxy.

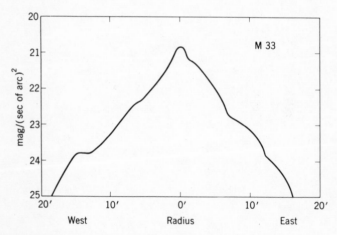

FIGURE 8.6   Profile of M 33 in blue light, obtained by De Vaucouleurs.

The globular clusters of M 33 are very much a source of mystery; they are quite anomalous when compared with those of M 31 or our Galaxy. The most conspicuous difference is in their apparent and absolute luminosities, which are at least two magnitudes fainter than one would expect. Of the 15 globular clusters identified as such by Hubble, none were as bright as the average for M 31. The colors of these clusters are also anomalous, in the sense that they are much bluer than the norm. It is believed that most of these objects are "blue globular clusters" of the type found in the Magellanic Clouds; that is, they are rich open clusters that appear to be globular only because of their large number of stars and large size. It is possible that five of the clusters (that are red) may be true globular clusters, but their luminosity is still anomalously low. Hiltner has estimated that the blue clusters need only be three or four times as rich as the Pleiades, an open cluster in our Galaxy.

Several measurements of the total mass of neutral hydrogen gas in M 33 have been made. The conclusion is that approximately 5 percent of the entire mass is in the form of H I. This is a sensibly larger amount than for M 31.

* 9 *   the sculptor
and
fornax galaxies

Two of the nearest and most thoroughly investigated elliptical galaxies are the Sculptor and Fornax dwarf galaxies. They are treated here in detail because they are interesting and well-studied examples of their class.

Both were discovered by Harlow Shapley, using plates from the Boyden Observatory, South Africa, in 1937 and 1938. They are exceedingly faint objects, too faint for it to be an easy matter to measure their total integrated brightness. Shapley estimated very roughly from Harvard plates that both have a total apparent magnitude of about 9. If we accept Shapley's rough estimate and use distances estimated in 1939 by Baade and Hubble (84 kpc for Sculptor and 188 kpc for Fornax), we find exceedingly faint absolute magnitudes for these galaxies. That for Sculptor turns out to be only −10.6 and that for Fornax −12.4, both of which are far fainter than for any galaxies discovered prior to 1939. More recently determined data on both the apparent magnitude and the distances of these systems confirm these conclusions (see Table 7.1).

Recent star counts made with plates taken by the ADH Baker-Schmidt telescope at Boyden Observatory have shown that the Sculptor system has a surprisingly large angular extent for so faint an object. Sculptor is elliptical in shape, with a ratio of axes of 0.65, and its major axis has a maximum extent of 1.5 deg (Figure 9.1).

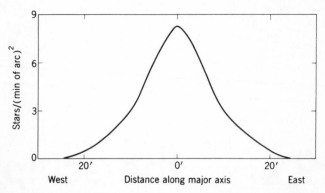

FIGURE 9.1   Profile of the Sculptor dwarf galaxy, from star counts on several plates.

Such a large apparent diameter, however, does not mean a large galaxy intrinsically. Its linear diameter calculated from the distance estimated by Baade and Hubble is only 2 kpc, meaning that it is one of the smallest galaxies known.

The radius of Sculptor has been estimated by fitting its major axis profile to a model by King for a gravitationally limited system. Comparison with King's model showed that Sculptor's size is gravitationally controlled by the tidal effects of our own massive Galaxy. Stars in the outer parts of Sculptor are lost to the system when the force on them exerted by our Galaxy exceeds that of the Sculptor system itself. The limiting radius, r_t, is related to the mass of the satellite galaxy, m, the mass of the larger galaxy, M, and the distance between the galaxies, D, by the relation

$$r_t = D \left(\frac{m}{3M} \right)^{1/3}$$

In the case of Sculptor, this theoretically computed radius is very nearly equal to the limiting radius derived from star counts.

A study of the structure of the Fornax galaxy showed that its

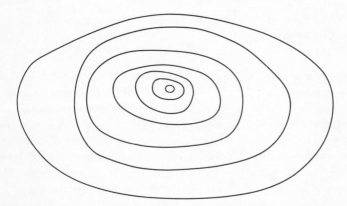

FIGURE 9.2   Isodents of the Fornax dwarf, plotted from star counts on an ADH Schmidt plate.

shape (Figure 9.2) is almost identical to that of the Sculptor system (the mean ratio of axes is 0.65) and the apparent diameter is 100 min of arc, leading to a linear diameter of 6 kpc. This is somewhat smaller than its computed tidally limiting radius.

A recent investigation of the color-magnitude diagram for the Sculptor galaxy shows that it is rather similar to globular clusters. The color-magnitude diagram can be measured for only the brightest stars with present equipment, but over the interval available it looks identical to that of a rich globular cluster (Figure 9.3). From

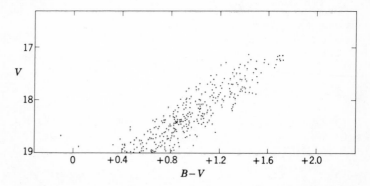

FIGURE 9.3   Color-magnitude diagram of the brightest stars in the Sculptor galaxy.

the slope of the giant branch, it has been possible to estimate that the chemical composition of most of the stars in the Sculptor galaxy is probably similar to that of M 3 or other globular clusters of moderate heavy-element deficiency. There are a few blue main sequence stars that may be members of the Sculptor system, but they do not seem to be any different from those few unexplained blue stars found in globular clusters. There is in fact no noticeable difference as far as the stars are concerned between the Sculptor galaxy and a normal globular cluster except that the density of stars is exceedingly low in the case of Sculptor. Its luminosity function is similar to but 15 times as rich as that of the globular cluster M 3 (Figure 9.4). The total number of RR Lyrae variables has been determined by Thackeray to be approximately 700, about five times the number in M 3.

The distance of the Fornax galaxy is sufficiently great that it is difficult to resolve into stars except on plates taken with the largest southern telescopes. RR Lyrae variables are probably at $m_V \approx 22.0$, beyond the limits of studies made so far, and only the brightest giant stars have been photographed and studied. However, there is one unusual feature of the Fornax galaxy that is a matter of interest. It

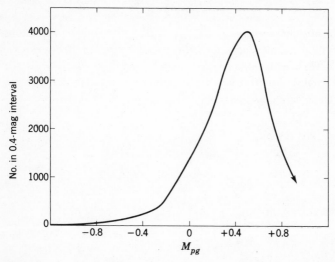

FIGURE 9.4   Luminosity function of the Sculptor galaxy, determined by Shapley.

contains five globular clusters, all very normal objects of their class. That the Fornax system should have globular clusters while the Sculptor system does not is probably a result of the larger mass of the Fornax system (about 2×10^7 solar masses, as opposed to 3×10^6 $M_{\odot}$ for Sculptor).

The clusters have two unusual features, both of which may be the result of Fornax's small size. First, the diameters of the clusters, though hard to define and measure accurately, seem to be between 5 and 10 times as big as for normal globular clusters of our Galaxy. This may be the result of the much smaller mass of Fornax, which has therefore, smaller tidal effects on its clusters than our Galaxy has on its globulars.

Also, there is the fact that the brightest star in the Fornax galaxy proper is about half a magnitude brighter than the brightest stars in its own globular clusters, suggesting that perhaps there is a difference in composition between the dwarf galaxy itself and globular clusters. To what extent this can be ascribed to a difference in composition, or to a spread in age for the galaxy itself, or to other causes can only be known when there is a very large telescope in the southern hemisphere. In the meantime it is safe to say that the Fornax galaxy, which bridges the gap between dwarf galaxies near enough to resolve and normal elliptical galaxies too far away to be studied in detail, may provide a clue to the mystery of the composition, age, and evolution of elliptical galaxies.

⁎ 10 ⁎

clusters
of
galaxies

A fairly large proportion of galaxies occur in clusters. Approximately 50 percent of all galaxies with red shifts of c $\Delta\lambda/\lambda < 1,000$ km/sec belong to such clusters, and the proportion may be larger when large-scale volumes of space are considered. Table 10.1 lists several well-known clusters.

TABLE 10.1   PROPERTIES OF SOME WELL-KNOWN CLUSTERS OF GALAXIES

NAME	DISTANCE, Mpc	DIAMETER, Mpc	DESCRIPTION
Local group	—	0.8	Small loose group
M 81 group	2.2	0.4	Loose group
Virgo cluster	11	2	Large complex cluster
Fornax cluster	13	1	Complex cluster
Coma cluster	50	7	Large compact cluster
Hercules cluster	74	2	Large loose cluster
Corona Borealis cluster	210	2	Compact cluster

TYPES OF CLUSTERS

Generally clusters of galaxies are divided into three types: small assemblages of mixed types of galaxies; larger, loosely structured aggregates of mixed types; and very large compact clusters of E and S0 galaxies. These are referred to in the following pages as "groups," "aggregates," and "giant clusters," respectively. Several attempts have been made to subdivide them further into 5 to 10 more types differing in size, structure, density, and type of population. Account can be taken of those with an apparently uniform surface density, those with a core and outer extensions, those with multiple concentrations, and those with highly regular shape and symmetry.

The reasons for the differences between clusters is not known. It was once thought that collisions could account for the prevalence of S0 galaxies in the high density clusters where the probability of collision would be greater than elsewhere. A mutual collision could clean out the dust and gas of two galaxies, for the stars would pass through unimpeded, while the dust and gas clouds would collide, heat up, and dissipate to intergalactic space. For a looser

cluster (an aggregate), the probability of collision would be lower,
so fewer galaxies in an aggregate would have lost their gas and
dust.

A possible example is shown in Figure 10.1, displaying the types
of galaxies in the Fornax cluster of galaxies, an aggregate with a
high-density core (not to be confused, of course, with the Fornax

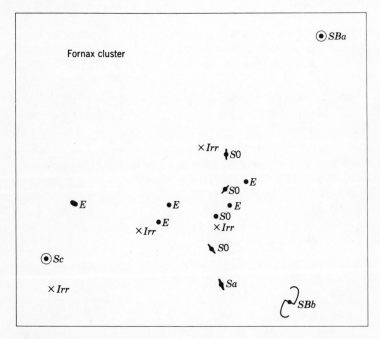

FIGURE 10.1 The distribution in the sky of galaxies of various types
belonging to the Fornax cluster.

galaxy of the last chapter). The S0 galaxies are strongly concentrated to the compact core, while the low-density outer parts of
the cluster contain normal spirals. This may be explained by the
effect of collisions in the core.

However, it should be mentioned that such collisions cannot be
the entire reason for the abundance of S0 galaxies in giant clusters,

as recent computations show that the collision probability during the lifetime of the universe is not large enough in most cases. Perhaps the initial conditions in the proto-cluster differed, so that high-density clusters tended to foster high-density galaxies.

DIMENSIONS

In size, clusters of galaxies range widely, from less than 100 kpc to more than 8,000 kpc. A well-known, very small group is Stefan's Quintet, with a mean diameter of only 50 kpc, and a total population of only four (the fifth galaxy of the "quintet" has turned out to be a nearer field galaxy). Among the largest clusters is the Coma cluster, over 7 Mpc in diameter and containing many thousands of galaxies.

The size-frequency relation for clusters of galaxies is not well-known, mainly because the size of a cluster is so hard to determine. Also, selection effects are important, as small and loose groups are more difficult to distinguish at large distances than giant clusters. The frequency-diameter relation probably is a smooth curve, running from large numbers for the smallest clusters to very small numbers for the giant clusters.

MASSES

There are two ways of estimating the total mass of a cluster of galaxies. The first is to assign a mass by some other method to each member galaxy and then add them up. In practice, this means measuring the luminosities of all members and then applying an assumed mass-light ratio for each. This method also means taking into account even those subluminous galaxies that may not be detected and any intergalactic dust or gas. There is considerable disagreement among astronomers about how much mass is involved in intergalactic matter in clusters of galaxies; intergalactic H I has been detected by some and disputed by others; the detection of intergalactic dust in some clusters is also controversial. Thus, this method can only give a rough and uncertain value for the total mass of a cluster.

The second method is to apply the virial theorem and to assume the cluster to be dynamically stable (see Chapter 5).

Total masses derived for clusters range from $\sim 10^{11}$ to 10^{15} solar masses; the upper limit is 10^{17} if the virial theorem is applied. Clusters of dwarf galaxies have been identified, and these may have masses of only $\sim 10^{9}$ suns.

DENSITIES

Knowing the sizes and masses of clusters allows computation of mean densities, although the large uncertainties involved in each of these data lead to very large uncertainties in the product. Computed densities range from high values of $\sim 10^{6}$ times the general field density for compact groups to only ~ 10 times the field density for the large, loose aggregates. The mean density for the Coma cluster, a typical "giant cluster" is about 10^{2} greater than the field. The large-scale mean density for the universe is $\sim 10^{-30}$ gm/cm^{3}, so that clusters of galaxies range in density from $\sim 10^{-29}$ to $\sim 10^{-23}$ gm/cm^{3}. These values (including the field density) are very uncertain and could be in error by more than an order of magnitude. Also, they do not take into account any possible intergalactic matter.

THE LUMINOSITY FUNCTION

The number of galaxies in each absolute magnitude interval is called the luminosity function. Our best information on the luminosity function for galaxies comes from study of clusters. It is too difficult to avoid serious errors due to selection effects if it is attempted to determine the luminosity function for field galaxies.

Zwicky has proposed that galaxies are most abundant at the fainter absolute magnitudes, and recent data from clusters tends to substantiate this hypothesis. Figure 10.2 shows the luminosity functions for three clusters: the local group, the Fornax cluster, and the rich cluster called Abell No. 1035 (from Abell's catalog of rich clusters). All three examples illustrate the trend toward large numbers of the faintest galaxies. It is not known whether this trend continues to smaller and smaller galaxies, eventually stopping with single stars, or whether there is a maximum point at ~ -10 absolute magnitude with fainter galaxies relatively rare. Such faint galaxies are difficult to detect even in the local group.

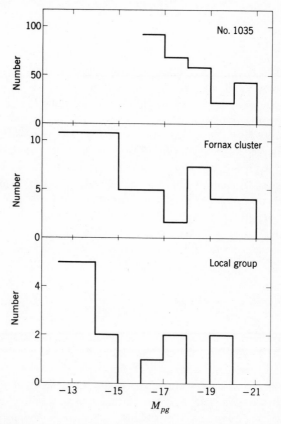

FIGURE 10.2   Luminosity functions of three clusters of galaxies.

Abell has found that the luminosity functions of giant clusters have certain fine structure that is reproducible from one cluster to the next. He has detected several slight "bumps" on the curves for many rich clusters, and suspects that these features occur always at the same absolute magnitudes. If so, they will be useful as accurate distance indicators for very distant clusters, an important fact for cosmological investigations.

It has been found that all types of galaxies do not exist in the same proportions everywhere under the luminosity function curve. For instance, there seem to be very few spiral galaxies fainter than $M = -16$ and very few irregular galaxies brighter than this. Most of the faintest known galaxies are ellipticals, and the very brightest known galaxies are also ellipticals. Figure 10.3 shows the types of

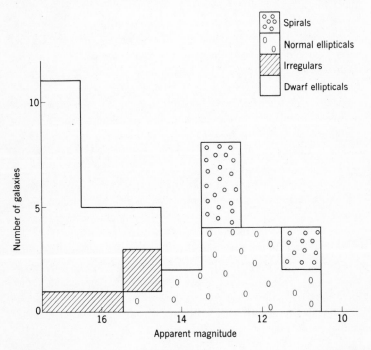

FIGURE 10.3 The types of galaxies that make up the Fornax cluster luminosity function.

galaxies that contribute to the different parts of the Fornax cluster luminosity fuction. Here, the spirals occupy a rather narrow range, the irregulars an even narrower one, and the ellipticals are preferentially either quite bright or very faint.

As discussed in Chapter 5 and above, the virial theorem has been applied to clusters of galaxies to determine their total masses. Since this leads to results that seem too big, it has been suggested that clusters of galaxies are not stable and thus the virial theorem does not apply. Ambartzumian believes it likely that clusters of galaxies are rapidly expanding, and that they will eventually dissipate into the intergalactic field. However, for the local group, which seems to be unstable if the virial theorem is applied to it, just the opposite is the case; the two most massive objects, M 31 and our Galaxy, which contain some 90 percent of the total mass of the group, are *approaching* each other. The local group, on the assumption of instability, would be contracting.

There is no known reason for either expansion or contraction of a cluster of galaxies on the short time scale required by the virial theorem (if the mass discrepancy is entirely due to instability). Galaxies cannot be expanding from a common cloud where they were formed, as was once suggested, because the expansion time scale is only $\sim 10^7$ years and most galaxies are certainly $\sim 10^{10}$ years old. Also, they cannot be all contracting under gravitational forces, because this would lead to the improbable conclusion that all clusters will collapse (simultaneously) $\sim 10^7$ years from now.

Instead, it is more probable that clusters of galaxies are stable, or nearly so, and that the virial theorem does not apply. Intergalactic matter and systematic effects (such as double galaxies with their large velocities of revolution) probably combine to produce the observed result. The last word on this subject, however, has certainly not been said.

SECOND-ORDER CLUSTERING

Are there clusters of clusters of galaxies? The answer to this difficult question is probably yes, but there is no general agreement among scientists. Certainly it is true that the clusters of galaxies are nonrandom in their distribution throughout the sky. Many scientists ascribe this fact to second-order clustering, but others believe that intergalactic absorption may be responsible.

A recent study by Abell showed that his large, very uniform

sample of rich clusters was highly nonrandom in its projected distribution. This nonrandomness was greatest when he studied them with a particular cell size, and this cell size was found to be correlated with distance. The most straightforward interpretation of this result is that second-order clustering is common and that the mean size of clusters of clusters is about 60 Mpc.

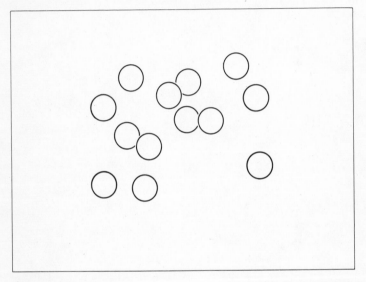

FIGURE 10.4   Locations of clusters in a cluster of clusters of galaxies discovered by Abell. This second-order cluster is 30 Mpc in diameter.

Shapley suggested that we are members of a "supercluster," consisting of the local group, the Virgo cluster, and several other nearby clusters. The size of the local supercluster is about 50 Mpc, according to De Vaucouleurs, who has reported that it is flattened and rotating.

A list of 17 other probable superclusters has been prepared by Abell. They contain from 6 to 29 clusters and have diameters ranging from 27 to 96 Mpc. Three of them lie near to a clustering of radio sources (Chapter 13) near the south galactic pole.

✳ **11** ✳   **the evolution
of
galaxies**

In the few years that have elapsed since 1950, astronomy has realized a profound, detailed, and undoubtedly generally correct understanding of stellar evolution. This has come about through the combination of highly refined techniques of measurement of stellar radiation combined with high-speed computer solutions of difficult problems in physics. The recent great advances in the understanding of stellar evolution make it now possible to investigate the evolution of galaxies.

EARLY THEORIES

Before astronomers really understood stellar evolution, there were two early and very tentative theories of the evolution of galaxies. Both of these theories are now known to be wrong, but it is useful to review them. The first theory was Hubble's. He believed that his classification sequence of galaxies was an evolutionary one (Chapter 2). Hubble thought it reasonable to believe that galaxies begin as large spherical objects looking like E0 galaxies. He proposed that rotation then causes galaxies, as they develop, to flatten out, changing gradually from E0 to E7. After becoming an E7 galaxy, an object develops spiral arms and flattens further, losing material from its central elliptical-like nucleus. At the end of this sequence are Sc galaxies with almost no nucleus and very extensive spiral arms, and the final stage occurs when all such structure disappears and there is nothing left but an irregular galaxy, devoid of pattern.

The other early theory of the evolution of galaxies was that suggested by Harlow Shapley. Shapley took exactly the opposite view from that of Hubble and proposed that galaxies begin life as irregular, formless masses and that as they evolve, form and structure gradually emerge. In his view the youngest galaxies are the irregular galaxies; these eventually change into the circular pattern of an Sc galaxy, and then slowly wind up to the Sb stage and the Sa stage. Finally the spiral arms disappear altogether leaving a perfectly symmetrical elliptical galaxy. Shapley's theory, like Hubble's, was proposed without any supporting physical arguments, primarily because the physical understanding of galaxies and stars at that time was not ready for such arguments. It, also like Hubble's, is now known to be wrong. Both of these early theories can be demonstrated to be in conflict with the facts of galactic dynamics and stellar evolution. In the following pages, our present understanding of the evolution of stars and the dynamics of galaxies is reviewed and applied to problems of the evolution of galaxies.

STELLAR EVOLUTION

It is now understood how stars evolve and change with time. The details of the pattern of stellar evolution depend upon the total mass of the star and on its chemical composition. However, the general pattern for all stars is the same.

Stars are formed from clouds of gas and dust which condense under their own gravitational potential. These clouds emit light as they condense and contract, converting gravitational energy to electromagnetic and thermal energy. The temperatures in the interiors of these "protostars," as they are often called, eventually reach large enough values that nuclear reactions can take place. When this occurs, the star gradually brightens, continuing to contract and to become hotter. It eventually reaches a point of equilibrium (called the *main sequence stage*) where the gravitational pull inward of the material in the star is exactly balanced by the outward pressure caused by the nuclear reactions occurring in its center. When this equilibrium is reached, the star's luminosity, temperature, and radius stay almost constant, and it remains near this equilibrium point for the major portion of its lifetime.

When most of the hydrogen in the center of a star is used up (converted to helium), the equilibrium is no longer maintained, and the core of the star contracts. This leads to an expansion of the outer envelopes of the star so that the star cools rapidly and grows in dimension. The star becomes what is called a *red giant,* with a very cool, large, red outer envelope. At this point in the star's history it begins to lose some of its mass, either by expelling streams of low velocity gas or by explosions. The mass loss continues until the total mass of the star is approximately that of the sun. If the mass of the star originally is smaller than that of the sun, very little mass loss occurs. When it reaches this critical mass, the star collapses. Most of its hydrogen has now been completely converted to helium and heavier elements, and so now it has no source of nuclear energy. It contracts until the matter is of exceedingly high density, with the nuclei and electrons almost in contact, a situation in which the matter is called *degenerate*. Its luminosity becomes almost negligible, and its size is on the order of those of planets. Because such "dead" stars have faintly glowing atmospheres at a moderately high temperature, they are called *white dwarf stars*. The white dwarfs represent the final stage of the pattern of evolution. Much of the material that was lost by the more massive stars is now able to reform as a new generation of stars which will have a slightly different composition because of the enrichment by the heavy elements formed in the first generation stars before their collapse.

A graphic demonstration of the pattern of stellar evolution is presented in Figure 11.1, which shows the relationship between the temperatures and luminosities of star clusters of three different ages. The youngest star cluster, h and χ Persei, has an age of only a few million years, and in it stars exist that are exceedingly hot and luminous. These stars cannot remain in their present condition long because of the high rate of loss of energy. The cool high-luminosity stars that are found in this cluster have already evolved away from the condition of equilibrium and are now red supergiant stars that will soon disappear as white dwarfs.

The cluster designated as M 11 is intermediate in age, 4×10^7 years. It does not have highly luminous stars, and many of its moderately luminous stars are in the red giant stage already.

The oldest cluster shown in Figure 11.1 is the cluster NGC 188, which has lost all of its hot stars brighter approximately than the luminosity of the sun. A large number of evolved red giant stars are found in this cluster, and it probably contains very many as yet undetected white dwarfs. From the location of the top of its main sequence, it is possible to find an age for it of approximately 10^{10} years.

All of these ages are derived by comparing the diagrams for the clusters shown in Figure 11.1 with detailed, very complicated astrophysical computations of evolutionary paths. Thus the process requires two astronomical research programs: (1) the temperatures, luminosities, and distances of the clusters must be measured at the telescope, and (2) theoretical calculations of the changes in stars of a wide variety of masses and chemical compositions must be

carried out, on high-speed computing machines, for comparisons
with the observations.

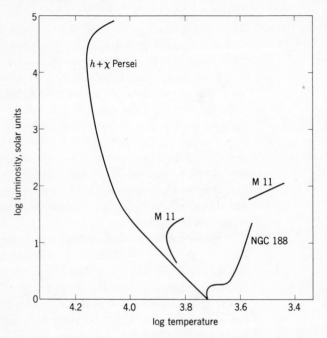

FIGURE 11.1   Composite temperature-luminosity diagram for three star
clusters of different ages.

EVOLUTION OF STAR GROUPS

From what we know of stellar evolution it is possible now to
outline the way in which a group of stars will evolve with time, at
least as far as the content of the star group is concerned. We find
from the sorts of considerations outlined above that the following
pattern is expected for a group of stars:

First Stage.   The object begins as a cloud of gas or gas and
                 dust, consisting primarily of hydrogen. This cloud

may have arisen as a gravitational condensation in a primordial gaseous cosmos. The physical details of such a condensation are still obscure and subject to argument.

Second Stage. When the gas cloud has contracted under its own gravitational potential to a point where it has a certain critical density, protostars can form and from these, eventually stars. During this stage the cluster consists of young stars, bright and blue, with considerable gas and dust.

Third Stage. As time elapses, the younger stars evolve away from the main sequence and become red giants and eventually white dwarfs. During this stage the cluster's brightest stars are yellowish and fairly bright. There is some gas left in the cluster, and this is enriched with heavy elements formed in the now evolved stars.

Fourth Stage. This stage is characterized by even fewer bright stars and by enrichment with heavy elements of the stars that are left. There is a larger number of white dwarfs and a smaller amount of gas. By this time a certain amount of dynamic relaxation has occurred and the cluster is likely to be fairly symmetrical in shape.

Fifth Stage. In the fifth and last stage, the cluster is enriched in heavy element abundance. It consists of only very old stars and a large number of white dwarfs, with no gas remaining.

The manifestation of this pattern in terms of observable quantities can now be predicted. First, in color, the age sequence is from blue to red, as the brightest stars, which contribute most of the light in the cluster, change in character from hot bright blue stars to the fainter red giants characteristic of the last stages. In the spectrum the young star groups show predominantly the spectra of the bright blue, luminous, metal-deficient main sequence stars. As evolution progresses, this gradually changes to the spectrum characteristic of low-luminosity, metal-rich giant stars. In the ratio of mass to luminosity, M/L, another important and measurable characteristic of a star group, the change is from large values when most of the mass is in the form of nonluminous gas, to small values when most of the luminosity is in the form of the very luminous young main sequence stars, to again large values when most of the mass is in the form of subluminous white dwarf stars. Finally, in the gas content the trend is from 100 percent gradually diminishing to 0 percent.

CONTENT OF GALAXIES

In Table 11.1 are gathered the relevant characteristics of the three main types of galaxies. A comparison of this table with the above considerations of evolutionary trends in groups of stars shows

TABLE 11.1   CONTENT OF GALAXIES

TYPE	OLD STARS	YOUNG STARS	COLOR	M/L	PERCENT H I
E	Almost all	None	Red	~50	0
S	Some	Some	Red and blue	~3	~1
Irr	A few	Many	Blue	~1	~10

that the sequence of elliptical to spiral to irregular galaxies is not at all an evolutionary sequence. The elliptical galaxies do seem to be old objects but the spiral and irregular galaxies also contain a certain number of stars of considerable age. Therefore a more reasonable picture is that the Hubble types make up a *conservation* classification rather than an evolutionary sequence. All of these galaxies contain old stars, and therefore none is necessarily younger than any other, but the rate at which stars have been formed and at which the gas has been exhausted has been different from one type to the other. The elliptical galaxies have used up all of the available building materials for stars, and no new stars are being formed or have been formed in recent times. The more conservative spiral galaxies have used up a large percentage of the available gas, but there is still some left which is forming new stars at the present time. The irregular galaxies have been most conservative with their raw materials; with still a large percentage of gas remaining they are rich in young, newly formed stars.

Our conclusions, then, are that the sequence of the classification of galaxies is not an evolutionary sequence, but that all of the galaxies of the sequence are old. The best evidence available now indicates that they are all of approximately the same age, at least all of those near enough to our Galaxy for this to be estimated. Since the difference between galaxies cannot be explained by their differences in age, we must look elsewhere for an explanation. Probably this explanation is connected with certian dynamical characteristics of galaxies, to be discussed next.

DYNAMICAL PROBLEMS

There are several important and interesting problems of galactic dynamics that bear very directly on our discussion of the evolution of galaxies. The first has to do with the processes involved in the initial condensation of matter into a galaxy. This is a moderately difficult mathematical problem, and recent results have produced models of the initial conditions in a contracting galaxy. One must assume certain characteristics of the protogalaxy, namely, its mass, density, radius, velocity of turbulence, temperature, and magnetic field. Then one finds that what happens to the gas cloud after instability sets in depends on the angular momentum of the cloud. First the cloud experiences free fall towards its center of mass. Then there is a choice depending on what the angular momentum is; if there is no angular momentum, then the body continues in a free fall towards its center of mass and eventually, when the velocity of the edge of the body exceeds the velocity of light, it disappears into a relativistic "hole." If the angular momentum is moderate, approximately 40 to 100 km/sec, then the gas cloud collapses until it reaches an "angular momentum barrier" when the angular momentum prevents further collapse and it reexpands to form a star cloud. Computations indicate that star formation begins before the angular momentum barrier is reached. Following this, mixing of orbits occurs. If the angular momentum is very large, rotation prevents a rapid collapse and the density is never very high, with the consequence that star formation is never rapid.

These considerations of the initial condensations of a protogalaxy suggest that the present state of elliptical and spiral galaxies may differ because of a difference in the original rotation velocity of the protogalaxy involved. A protogalaxy which eventually becomes an elliptical galaxy has only moderate angular momentum at the beginning. Therefore most of its material forms into stars early in its history when its density is very high, before the angular momentum barrier stops its collapse. For a protogalaxy with much larger angular momentum, the angular momentum barrier is reached much sooner, before the density is high enough for more than just a few stars to be formed. Therefore star formation proceeds from then on much more slowly. These conclusions rest on the assumption (supported by observations in our Galaxy) that the rate of star formation is dependent strongly on the density of the raw material.

Another important dynamical problem having to do with the development of galaxies involves the spiral arms. It is not known how spiral arms are able to maintain themselves. The rotation times for spiral galaxies are approximately 10^8 years, halfway out from the center, but the ages of the spiral galaxies are approximately 10^{10} years. Therefore, one would expect that a spiral arm formed at the beginning of the galaxy's history would now be wound up 100 times. In actual fact most spiral arms of galaxies show only one or two complete turns. Therefore they must either be "frozen in," perhaps by magnetic fields, or else they must regenerate themselves in some way. A possible regenerating process might be the occasional explosions, still unexplained, which are known to occur in some galaxies (Chapter 13).

Another important dynamical problem that is not solved is the problem of explaining the existence of the bars in the barred spiral galaxies. These masses of stars do not obey any reasonable dynamical model and may be held in place by some nongravitational force such as a strong magnetic field. Just how this can work is not yet known.

A further dynamical problem that has been investigated is the problem of the relaxation of galaxies. The dynamical relaxation of a galaxy is achieved when all the stars of a galaxy have suffered sufficient encounters with other stars so that any original orbit is now completely erased. The formula for calculating this relaxation time is as follows:

$$T = 1.12 \times 10^{13} \frac{[\overline{v^2}]^{3/2}}{Nm^2 \log [9.3 \times 10^4 \, Dv^2/2m]}$$

where v = velocity in units of 20 km/sec

D = mean distance between stars in parsecs

m = typical mass of a star

N = star density in number of stars per cubic parsec

When this formula is applied to dwarf elliptical galaxies, the relaxation time is found to be 10^{13} years, a thousand times the actual age of the system, which therefore cannot be a true dynamically relaxed system. Stellar encounters cannot explain the symmetry and regular shape of such a galaxy. Instead it may be that it became dynamically relaxed when it existed for a brief period as a group of gas clouds which experienced physical encounters and collisions. In this type of galaxy, perhaps, its present shape and organization were determined in its very earliest stage.

RECENT EVOLUTION OF GALAXIES

For the nearest galaxies it is possible to measure the colors and brightnesses of stars to limits fainter than absolute magnitude ~ 0. It is thus possible in principle to explore the recent evolutionary history of such a galaxy by measuring the color-magnitude diagrams of various regions in the galaxy and determining their ages. This works only when a galaxy is sufficiently simple to be broken up into groups that can be dated reliably; such galaxies do exist among the dwarf irregular galaxies of the local group. Figure 11.2 shows the recent evolution of the galaxy IC 1613, established by measurement of the color-magnitude diagrams, the luminosity functions, and the surface brightness of various recognizable components of the system. Because of its distance, it is only possible to examine the last 10^8 years of this galaxy. Older stars are too faint to be measured with present techniques. The most important and surprising result of such investigations is that in many cases the small irregular gal-

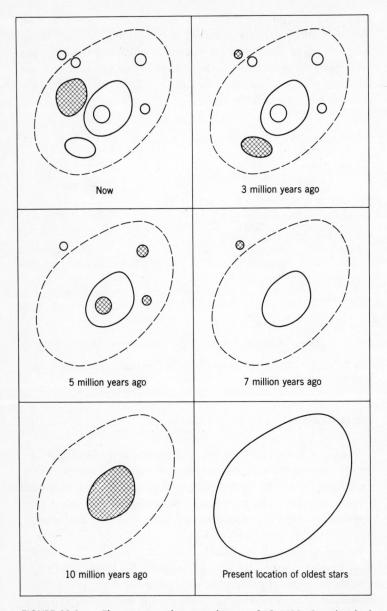

Now

3 million years ago

5 million years ago

7 million years ago

10 million years ago

Present location of oldest stars

FIGURE 11.2 The recent evolutionary history of IC 1613. Cross-hatched areas indicate locations of new star formation.

✳   the evolution of galaxies

axies have changed drastically in a relatively short period of time. Two particularly dramatic examples of this are IC 1727 and Holmberg II, both of which have large areas in which star formation has been going on as recently as the last million or so years. It is not known how this recent star formation can be reconciled with the probable large age of the systems.

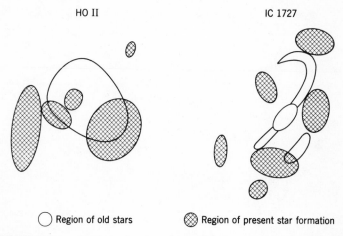

FIGURE 11.3   Regions of current formation of stars in the irregular galaxies Ho II and IC 1727.

VIOLENT EVENTS

There are increasing numbers of examples of galaxies that are experiencing or have experienced violent explosive events. These are detected primarily by the radio radiation received from them. There is certainly a drastic effect on the evolution of a galaxy that experiences such a gigantic explosion as the one that has recently occurred in M 82 (Chapter 14).

Recent discovery of very small, extremely luminous ($M_V \approx -26$) objects called *quasi-stellar galaxies* suggests that there may be observable examples of galaxies forming (or collapsing). It is not yet known just what these remarkable objects are, but the fact that they all have strong optical emission lines and some have strong radio emission indicates that an extremely energetic (and short-lived) event has occurred.

12 the
extragalactic
distance scale

One of the most important problems of astronomy is the establishment of distance indicators that can be used to gauge the vast scale of the universe. The problem must be solved in steps; various methods used are applicable only to restricted ranges in distance, so one is used to calibrate the next, and so forth. Objects the absolute luminosity of which can be calibrated geometrically in our Galaxy are used to establish distances for the nearest galaxies, and then very luminous objects in them are used to get distances of farther galaxies, until finally distances of the farthest observable galaxies are obtained. Fairly large uncertainties in these largest distances result from the addition of uncertainties in each step of the process.

Figure 12.1 schematically illustrates the method of establishing the extragalactic distance scale. The figure shows clearly how the entire structure depends ultimately on geometrical measurements for nearby stars.

In principle there are five separate regions of the universe in which the different distance scale indicators are used and calibrated. The first is the stellar environment of the sun in which the geometrical methods are used. Here both individual stellar parallaxes and moving cluster parallaxes are the important and fundamental distance indicators. The second portion of the universe is our Galaxy, particularly the subsystem of clusters of stars, in which further calibration of particular types of stars, such as variable stars, is carried out. Here the calibration is based on the location of the main sequence, determined from the local geometrical distance measures. The third portion of the universe is the local group of galaxies, in which the variable stars and similar objects calibrated in clusters of our Galaxy are observed and used for determining distances to nearby galaxies. The fourth area of the universe consists of the nearby clusters of galaxies, especially the Virgo cluster, where distances can still be determined by means of individual stars and other resolved objects. Here the distances are measured by comparison with similar objects in the local group galaxies. The fifth portion of the universe is that remaining, namely, the expanse of very distant galaxies, distances to which are measured either by their radial velocities or by their apparent magnitudes or other integrated properties.

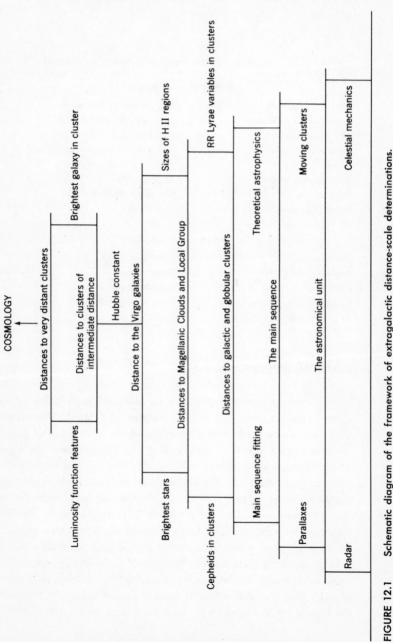

FIGURE 12.1 Schematic diagram of the framework of extragalactic distance-scale determinations.

Table 12.1 lists the many different distance indicators that have been or potentially could be used for determining distances to galaxies.

TABLE 12.1   POSSIBLE EXTRAGALACTIC DISTANCE INDICATORS

INDIVIDUAL OBJECTS

Classical cepheids	Main sequence fitting
Population II cepheids	Luminosity function fitting
RR Lyrae variables	Globular cluster giants
Long period variables	Spectral luminosity classification
Novae	Sizes of emission objects
Supernovae, type I	Brightest stars
Supernovae, type II	Planetary nebulae
Bright blue variables	

INTEGRATED METHODS

Radial velocities	Spectral criteria
Apparent magnitudes	Sizes
Colors	Luminosity classification
Cluster luminosity functions	Surface brightnesses
Brightest galaxies in clusters	

CLASSICAL CEPHEID VARIABLES

The cepheid variable stars can be observed in galaxies up to distance moduli of $m - M = 28$ (a distance of 4 Mpc). This means that they can be studied in all members of the local group of galaxies that contain them, as well as in a few galaxies near the local group. The period-luminosity relationship for cepheid variables is now well established for the Galaxy from measurements in clusters for which accurate distances can be determined by photometry of the main sequence stars. Thus, if one is willing to make the assumption that the cepheid variables are identical in other galaxies to those in ours, a measurement of period and luminosity for a number of cepheids in another galaxy will immediately provide an accurate distance, if colors can be measured to provide an estimation of reddening and absorption. So far, the period-luminosity relations are known for five galaxies in the local group: M 31, LMC, SMC,

IC 1613, and NGC 6822. It has been found that cepheid variables
with very large ranges define a narrow period-luminosity relationship, such that if only large-range cepheids are considered, great
accuracy can be obtained in the estimate of distance.

From measurements of five cepheid variables in the star clusters
of the Galaxy, Kraft has shown that the period-luminosity relationship has the form:

$$\overline{M_B} = -1.33 - 2.25 \log P$$

where $\overline{M_B}$ is the mean absolute magnitude measured in blue and P
is the period in days.

Figure 12.2 shows the period-luminosity relationship measured
for variable stars in the Small Magellanic Cloud by Arp. The best
fit for this relationship is a straight line of the following form:

$$\overline{B} = 17.45 - 2.25 \log P$$

where corrections for absorption and reddening have been made.
The slope of the line is exactly the same as that found in our Gal-

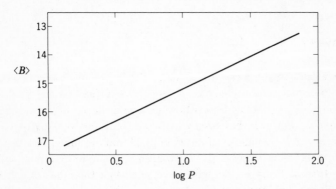

FIGURE 12.2   The period-luminosity relation for the Small Magellanic
Cloud. (After Arp.)

axy, and this is primarily due to the fact that in our Galaxy the slope
is difficult to determine and some reliance was put on what had

been found for the SMC. A comparison of the two period-luminosity relations leads to a distance modulus of 18.78 for the SMC.

RR LYRAE STARS

It is found by very accurate photometry of the main sequences of globular clusters in our Galaxy that all RR Lyrae stars have the same absolute magnitude, approximately $M_V = +0.5 \pm 0.2$. Thus these objects are extremely useful distance indicators for galaxies in which they can be measured. Unfortunately, RR Lyrae variables are not superluminous objects, and they can be seen only in the very nearest galaxies, with distance moduli less than 22 mag. So far RR Lyrae variables have been discovered in seven members of the local group of galaxies: the LMC, the SMC, Sculptor, Leo I, Leo II, Draco, and Ursa Minor. Accurate photometry of the RR Lyrae variables is available only for four of these galaxies: the SMC, Sculptor, Draco, and Ursa Minor. The only galaxy for which RR Lyraes and cepheids have both been measured is the SMC, and the distances determined in the two ways agree well.

NOVAE

Galaxies in the local group, and including more distant objects up to distances of as much as 10 Mpc, have novae that can be discovered at maximum with existing telescopes. Accurate photometry of novae, however, has been carried out only for M 31. Arp has observed a large number of novae in M 31 and has found that there is a relationship between the apparent magnitude of maximum and the time of decay of the light curve, such that those galaxies that reach the brightest maximum luminosities decay the most rapidly. Accurate photometry of some of these galaxies indicates that for novae of about five days duration the maximum apparent luminosity is $B = 15.8$. If the life-luminosity relationship for the 30 novae measured by Arp in M 31 is fitted to that for novae in our Galaxy for which accurate distances are known, the distance modulus to M 31 is derived to be 24.6 ± 0.3. This is in excellent agreement with the distance determined from cepheids. For other galaxies, novae have been observed but accurate photometry has not been carried out yet. The Magellanic Clouds have each had a few novae in the past, and novae have been observed in M 33. However, other members of the local group are apparently of too low a mass to have novae frequently enough to have been observed.

Novae are potentially very useful distance indicators for galaxies just outside the local group, such as those in the M 81 or M 101 groups where they will appear at about the 17th or 18th apparent magnitude. The difficulty in observing them arises from the fact that they occur predominately in the central bulge of a spiral galaxy, where the background intensity of stars is high enough to interfere seriously with detection and photometry.

H II REGIONS

A geometrical distance indicator is the angular size of H II regions. Sersic and Sandage have each used this method to obtain distances to galaxies up to distances as great as 10 Mpc. These astronomers found that the sizes of H II regions for nearby galaxies for which distances are known by other means are remarkably similar. That is, the largest H II regions in a galaxy seem to be the same size from galaxy to galaxy. A detailed discussion of this shows that there is a variation in the sizes of H II regions for galaxies of different total mass and of different Hubble types, but that for a given mass within each classification there is remarkable agreement on the intrinsic size of the largest regions. For instance, Sandage has shown that the largest H II region of a normal Sc or irregular galaxy has a linear mean dimension of approximately 245 parsecs, while the mean diameter of the five largest H II regions in such a galaxy is approximately 175 parsecs. These values were obtained by using local-group galaxies.

Distances to more distant galaxies can be obtained simply by measuring the angular diameters of the largest H II regions and comparing them with the calibrated known intrinsic sizes. This method has a great advantage over photometric methods in that no highly accurate photometry is needed and no correction need be made for reddening and absorption. However, the assumption must be made that the sizes of H II regions continue to be uniform from galaxy to galaxy when large samples of galaxies are measured. The difficulties of this method are connected with the fact that H II regions must be completely resolved by the telescope, meaning that only the very largest telescopes available can be used, and that Hα filters must be used in obtaining plates so that H II regions can be clearly separated from stellar associations or other star aggregates.

BRIGHTEST STARS

It is found that the absolute magnitudes of the brightest stars in a galaxy reach a certain upper limit, which can be used as a distance indicator for galaxies that are resolved into stars. The brightness of the brightest stars is a function of the type of galaxy and of its absolute magnitude, and therefore to calibrate this distance criterion one needs a fairly large sample of galaxies.

So far, calibration has been carried out in the local group and in two nearby groups, that around M 81 and that around M 101. Distances to these galaxies have been determined by one of the methods above, and the absolute magnitudes of the brightest stars in 30 galaxies belonging to these groups have been calibrated. The absolute blue magnitude of the brightest stars in galaxies is always between -7 and -10. The mean for all galaxies for which this measurement has been carried out is -9.3 ± 0.5. Most of the dispersion is due to the large range in total number of stars for the galaxies used to calibrate, which range in absolute magnitude from -14 to -20.

The brightest stars in a galaxy can be discerned as far away as the Virgo cloud, although for such large distances great care must be exercised in distinguishing an individual star from a clump of stars, an association or an H II region. The distance scale calibration that Hubble carried out in 1936 was greatly in error because he misidentified objects in distant galaxies as brightest stars when in fact they were associations and emission regions. In general, in the Virgo group H II regions do sometimes appear almost stellar on good plates taken with a large telescope; they are up to 1.8 mag brighter than the brightest stars in the galaxies. Therefore extreme care must be exercised to distinguish between stars and nonstellar

objects in distant galaxies when the brightest stars are used as a
distance criterion.

Of course, there is also the uncertainty due to the fact that the brightness of the brightest star is a function of the absolute magnitude of the galaxy, and the absolute magnitude of the galaxy is not known until its distance is determined. For that reason, this criterion is primarily useful for galaxies in groups where some idea of the relative absolute magnitudes of different members can be obtained.

LUMINOSITY FUNCTIONS OF CLUSTERS OF GALAXIES

For galaxies that are too far away for any of the above distance indicators to be resolved, other methods must be used. Supernovae, of course, can be seen in galaxies to very great distances. However, the intrinsic range in absolute magnitude for supernovae is so large (3 or 4 mag) that they are not at the present suitable for accurate distance determinations for galaxies.

A better method of obtaining distances to very distant galaxies is the method of the fitting of luminosity functions of clusters of galaxies. It is found that when very large clusters of galaxies are considered, the brightest galaxies are nearly the same in total absolute magnitude. This is a similar argument to that for the brightest star criterion, and it has many of the same problems. For instance, the brightest galaxy in a cluster is probably a function of the total number of galaxies or the total mass of the cluster. For very distant galaxies we would tend to pick up clusters with abnormally luminous galaxies as their brightest members, and we would thus pick out preferentially the largest and most populous clusters. A systematic error could be introduced in this way.

However, Abell has found evidence that the luminosity function is not smooth and that there are small maxima at specific absolute magnitudes. If this proves to be true in general, then the luminosity function method is the most powerful for determining accurate distances to the very distant galaxies. The brightest galaxy in the most distant clusters observed optically have apparent magnitudes of approximately 22, and it is found that the brightest galaxies in a cluster have absolute magnitudes of approximately -21, so that the distance modulus to these very distant clusters is on the order of $m - M = 43$, $(4 \times 10^9 \text{ parsecs})$.

RADIAL VELOCITIES

When the first measurements of the velocities of galaxies were made, it was discovered that for the fainter galaxies the Doppler shifts in the spectrum indicated extremely large velocities of recession. As Figure 12.3 demonstrates, the logarithm of the Doppler shift is roughly proportional to the apparent magnitude of the galaxy. This has been interpreted as an indication that the actual velocity of a galaxy is directly proportional to its distance, a fact that is corroborated by the study of clusters of galaxies, where distances can be measured with some confidence.

By studying nearby groups of galaxies as well as distant clusters, it is found that galaxies have peculiar motions (individual motions unrelated to the general trend of velocity) of the order of 100 to 300 km/sec. Superimposed on these peculiar motions is a general systematic expansion of the system of galaxies, and the velocities of expansion range from values near zero for the nearest galaxies up to values almost as large as the velocity of light for the very most distant objects detected. The constant of proportionality between the velocity of recession and the distance to a galaxy is called the Hubble constant, usually abbreviated by H. One of the major goals of the extragalactic distance scale is the calibration of the Hubble constant by means of measurements of the sort described in the sections above.

Most of the recent determinations of the Hubble constant have been derived by studies of the Virgo cloud of galaxies. The mean velocity of galaxies in the Virgo cloud is $+1136$ km/sec. This is a large enough value that peculiar motions are not important, a point that is extremely important. It is found that radial velocities for galaxies much closer than the Virgo cloud are not clearly related to the distance because of the fact that the systematic velocities are not sufficiently larger than the peculiar velocities. The most recent determinations of the value of the Hubble constant, H, place it in the range between 75 and 125 km/(sec)(Mpc). The most commonly quoted value at the time of the writing of this chapter is 100 km/(sec)(Mpc). This places the Virgo cloud at a distance of 11.36 Mpc. A great deal of work on this subject is being carried out at present, and in the next few years it is hoped that the Hubble con-

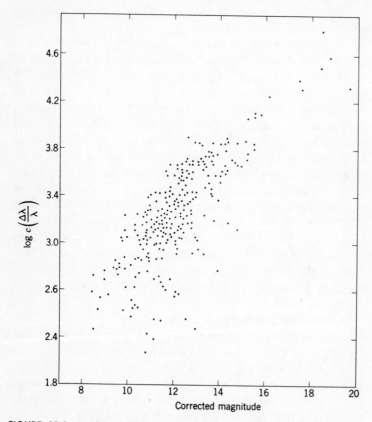

FIGURE 12.3   Plot of red shift versus apparent bolometric magnitude for galaxies. (After Humason, Mayall, and Sandage.)

stant will be determined with higher precision, especially through the application of more highly accurate photometry of nearby galaxies.

The radial velocity of a galaxy can be used as an indication of its distance in the range of velocities from 1,000 km/sec recession up to about 100,000 km/sec. Beyond these values, various cosmological theories predict different relationships between distance and velocity of expansion, and therefore the velocity-distance relation is undetermined until we are able to establish the appropriate cosmological model for the universe.

From measurements of absorption lines (usually the H and K lines of ionized calcium), velocities can be detected for galaxies as far away as 600 Mpc. The Hydra cluster has a velocity of 60,000 km/sec, and the absorption lines of its galaxies' spectra are just at the limit of detectability on spectra taken with the 200-in. telescope at Palomar. The brightest galaxy in the Hydra cluster has a visual magnitude of 17.7, considerably above the limit of detectability of a galaxy image on a plate. Larger distances can be measured by either using galaxies with bright emission lines, such as radio galaxies, or by using a narrow-band photoelectric filter technique, as employed by Baum. The most distant "normal" (not quasi-stellar) radio galaxy to have its velocity measured is one detected by Minkowski to have a radial velocity of 120,000 km/sec (0.46 times the velocity of light). The radial velocities of galaxies in the cluster to which this radio galaxy belongs were also measured photoelectrically by Baum, who similarly found the velocity of recession to be 120,000 km/sec.

An important breakthrough in the problem of detecting very distant objects occurred when the quasi-stellar radio sources were discovered in 1962. These objects have absolute magnitudes as bright as $M = -26$, and because they have bright emission lines, their radial velocities can be measured at extremely great distances. At the time of this writing, the most distant quasi-stellar radio source has a red shift of 2.0 ($\Delta\lambda/\lambda = 2.0$), indicating that its velocity of recession with respect to our Galaxy is 0.8 the velocity of light. When a good method is found to estimate distances to such objects independently of their velocities, the velocity-distance relation determined will very likely lead to a solution of the cosmological problem (Chapter 14).

13 extragalactic radio radiation

Radiation from extragalactic sources has been detected both in the emission line of hydrogen and in the continuum. The amount of emission in the 21-cm line of hydrogen depends, of course, on the amount of neutral hydrogen present in the galaxy. The continuum radiation, however, is less easily understood and explained. Various rather spectacular theories have been suggested to account for the strong "radio galaxies," which are currently among the most exciting and controversial objects in astronomy.

NEUTRAL HYDROGEN STUDIES

In 1944 the astronomer Van de Hulst suggested that interstellar hydrogen gas might radiate energy at radio wavelengths. The hydrogen atom has two hyperfine energy levels that have an energy difference corresponding to radiation of 21-cm wavelength. The half-life of the higher energy state is 10^7 years, so that only hydrogen atoms in very rarefied areas, such as the interstellar medium, can naturally emit this radiation. In dense gas clouds collisions are greatly more frequent than this. Several years after Van de Hulst's suggestion, the 21-cm hydrogen line was detected and identified as coming from the disk of the Milky Way. Subsequent study has led to more complete and more accurate ideas about the structure of our Galaxy than had been possible in the past. Now, also, 21-cm emission from other galaxies is breaking new ground.

The Detection of Neutral Hydrogen in Galaxies. The 21-cm emission line of hydrogen is very weak because of the long lifetime of the transition producing it. Therefore it is detectable so far only for the nearest galaxies (Figure 13.1). Table 13.1 lists those galaxies for which H I has been detected by radio means. Most of them are within 5,000 kpc.

One of the most striking features of this list is the fact that all galaxies are "late-type" objects, either loose spiral or irregular galaxies. This follows the expectation from optical work on them, which indicates larger amounts of gas than for E, S0, or Sa galaxies. No H I has been detected in galaxies of these three types, and measured upper limits indicate that very little can exist in them.

TABLE 13.1   **GALAXIES WITH H I DETECTED (AFTER EPSTEIN)**   141

GALAXY	$M_{H\,I}/M$	GALAXY	$M_{H\,I}/M$
NGC 55	0.10	NGC 3034	0.07
IC 10	0.20	NGC 3109	0.28
NGC 224	0.01	Sextans	0.10
NGC 247	0.04	IC 2574	0.07
SMC	0.20	NGC 4214	0.30
NGC 300	0.12	NGC 4244	0.04
IC 1613	0.22	NGC 4449	0.11
NGC 598	0.09	NGC 4631	0.14
NGC 628	0.14	NGC 4656	0.19
IC 342	0.12	NGC 5194	0.01
LMC	0.04	NGC 5236	0.04
NGC 2403	0.04	NGC 5457	0.06
HO II	0.21	NGC 6822	0.10
NGC 3031	0.01	NGC 6946	0.12

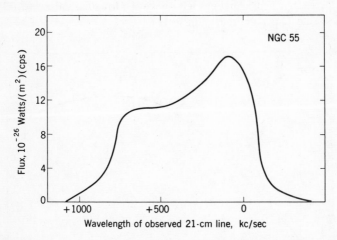

FIGURE 13.1   Scan of the galaxy NGC 55 in the 21-cm line of H I.
(After Epstein.)

The Ratio of Gas to Total Mass. It is possible to measure the total amount of neutral hydrogen gas in a galaxy if the 21-cm line is detected and if it is assumed to be optically thin, which is usually the case. The masses thus derived range from 6×10^7 solar masses for IC 1613 to 10^{10} suns for NGC 5457. An interesting datum is the ratio of H I mass to total mass. This tells to what extent the gas of a galaxy has been depleted by star formation and bears directly on its past and future. Table 13.1 summarizes these data for all available cases and shows that the relative amount of gas is strongly correlated with galaxy type. The *Sb* galaxies have small values of $M_{H\,I}/M$, about 0.01, while irregular galaxies have ratios as high as 0.30.

This agrees with the ideas of Chapter 11, which picture *Sc* and *Irr* galaxies as objects in which star formation from the original gas cloud has been slow and incomplete, while the *E, Sa,* and *Sb* are galaxies which have used up most of their gas in an early and efficient burst of forming of stars. It is possible from the gas–total-mass ratio to gain some idea of how conservative a certain galaxy has been with its raw materials. For instance, M 31 has only about 1 percent of its original gas left, while the irregular galaxy IC 1613 has some 22 percent remaining as H I.

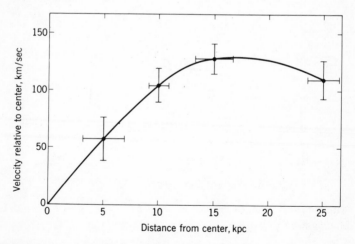

FIGURE 13.2   Rotation curve for NGC 55, determined from the 21-cm line.

Rotation Curves. For galaxies large and near enough, the 21-cm–line emission can be used to give rotation curves for the rotating

disks of neutral hydrogen. Comparisons with rotation curves for the
stars in these galaxies are difficult to obtain, but it is quite clear
that the two (stars and gas) move together in space, as would be
expected. Rotation curves obtained by radio means can be used
to calculate masses of galaxies (Chapter 5). Figure 13.2 shows an
H I rotation curve obtained for NGC 55, a *Sc* galaxy.

Distribution of Gas. Galaxies that are sufficiently well resolved can
be studied in detail to determine the spatial distribution of gas
within them. Such studies have been carried out so far for only a
very few objects. Figure 13.3 shows how the H I is distributed as

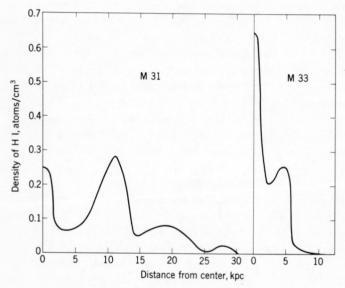

FIGURE 13.3   Radial distribution of H I in M 31 and M 33.

a function of distance from the center of M 31 and M 33, assuming the thickness of the gas disk to be 1 kpc. The two curves are
very different and have fine structure indicating concentration of
gas in spiral arms. This same type of concentration in arms is con-

spicuous for our Galaxy. A displacement of the gas arms of M 31 with respect to the stellar arms near M 32 has been detected and may be due to interaction of the two galaxies (discussed in Chapter 8).

NORMAL CONTINUUM EMISSION FROM GALAXIES

A survey of a large sample of bright galaxies recently has shown that most galaxies are weak radiators of continuum radio radiation. Half of the galaxies brighter than $m_{pg} = 11$ were detected, and many of the rest may well be radiating just below the detection limit. Thus radio galaxies are not peculiar, but quite normal. The unusual ones are so because of their abnormally high rate of radio emission.

The E and S0 galaxies are the weakest radio emitters. Only a few have been detected at all, and, except for peculiar ones, they are among the intrinsically weakest radio galaxies detected. The normal E galaxy radio emitters do not appear to be double sources, as is common for the peculiar E galaxies that are strong radio emitters. There is some evidence that E and S0 galaxies with detectable emission lines in their optical spectra (Chapter 3) are likely to have detectable continuum radio emission.

The spiral and irregular (type I) galaxies are much stronger radio sources, intrinsically, than the early types. The recent surveys suggest that all S and Irr I galaxies are radio emitters. Most of them have about the same ratio of visual to radio energy output; that is, the radio brightness is roughly proportional to the optical brightness for all but the peculiar, strong sources. The Sa galaxies are the weakest radio emitters, and the relative strength increases along the sequence Sa, Sb, Sc, Irr I.

The rate of emission of radio energy from normal radio galaxies is in the range 10^{37} to 10^{39} ergs/sec in the radio region. It is believed that much of this energy has a nonthermal source, associated with remnants of supernova explosions. The energy comes from synchrotron emission from relativistic electrons, probably accelerated in magnetic fields and produced by supernovae. Spiral galaxies may have a halo of tenuous relativistic gas surrounding them, emitting synchrotron radiation. Figure 13.4 shows the radio emission from M 31. The minimum total energies required for acceleration of the particles believed responsible for radio emission of normal galaxies 145 have been found by Burbidge to be about 10^{56} ergs.

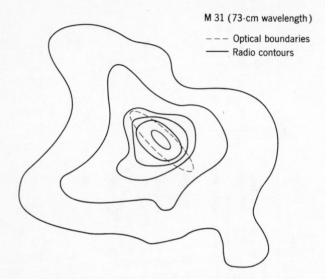

M 31 (73-cm wavelength)

– – – Optical boundaries
――― Radio contours

FIGURE 13.4   Continuum radio emission from M 31.

STRONG RADIO SOURCES

Although almost all galaxies radiate energy in the radio spectrum region, a few are unusually strong sources, emitting radio radiation at rates orders of magnitude greater than for normal galaxies. These are called "strong radio sources" or "radio galaxies." Table 13.2 lists some well-studied examples and summarizes their properties.

Shape and Size. The strong radio sources have been found often to be unusually large and double. About 50 percent of all strong sources that have so far been observed are larger than the optically visible galaxy. Of these, about 80 percent are double, with two distinct areas of radio emission detectable on each side of the visually observed galaxy image. The remainder are either single sources

TABLE 13.2 SOME STRONG RADIO SOURCES

NAME	OPTICAL DESCRIPTION	RADIO LUMINOSITY, ergs/sec	RADIO DIAMETER	OPTICAL DIAMETER	DISTANCE, Mpc
Virgo A (M87)	Elliptical galaxy with "jet" from nucleus	5×10^{41}	10' (and 30" jet)	10' (and 20" jet)	11
Fornax A (NGC 1316)	S0 galaxy with dust lanes and outer ring	6×10^{41}	30' (double)	15'	10
Centaurus A (NGC 5128)	Peculiar spiral	8×10^{41}	10° (multiple)	20'	4
Perseus A (NGC 1275)	Complex S0 galaxy	10^{42}	4' (with 10" core)	2'	70
Hydra A	Large S0 galaxy	2×10^{43}	50"	0'.5	210
Hercules A	Large S0 galaxy with dust lanes and outer wisps	1.5×10^{44}	110' (double)	0'.2	610
Cygnus A	Double galaxy	5×10^{44}	106" (double)	2"	220
3 C 48	Quasi-stellar source, fluctuations in brightness	5×10^{44}	<1"	<0".5	1,100

or combinations of a high-intensity central source and an extensive
outer halo.

In size, the radio sources range from below limits of present radio
telescopes up to values 100 times the sizes of normal galaxies. The
smallest detected sources are only 1,000 parsecs, or less, in diameter,
while the largest are nearly 10^6 parsecs across (Figure 13.5). This

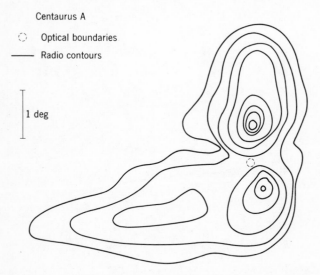

FIGURE 13.5   Continuum radio emission from the immense radio source
Centaurus A (NGC 5128 is the galaxy at the center of the source). (After
Bolton and Clark.)

wide range in size may be explained in terms of different ages, the
largest being the oldest; for in the case of the oldest, the material
emitting radio radiation has had time to expand outward from the
parent galaxy to great distances.

Radio Spectrum. The radio spectrum of most extragalactic radio
sources is relatively flat (Figure 13.6). This is interpreted to be
confirmation of the hypothesis that this radiation is emitted by the
synchrotron process, by relativistic, high-velocity electrons. For

those anomalous galaxies with curved spectra, the source may be deficient in the very highest energy electrons ($E > 3 \times 10^9$ eV). Polarization of several sources has been detected, confirming the synchrotron hypothesis.

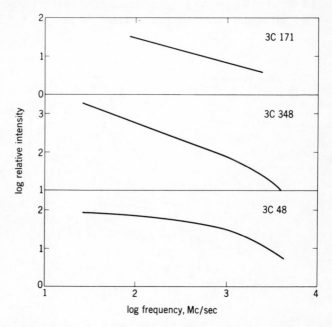

FIGURE 13.6   Radio spectra of some extragalactic sources.

Optical Nature. Almost all of the galaxies that have been identified as strong radio sources are peculiar in optical appearance. Their optical forms seem to fall into the following categories:

1. Elliptical galaxies with anomalous structure in the nuclear region, such as a bright "jet" of polarized light.
2. S0 galaxies with unusually gradual luminosity gradients. These are often the brightest galaxy of a cluster.
3. Galaxies with large amounts of dust obscuring their true shape.
4. Multiple galaxies with double nuclei or bright, interacting companions.
5. Galaxies with intense, starlike nuclei and faint outer envelopes.
6. Quasi-stellar objects with little or no resolvable detail.

In general, the most intense sources are the quasi-stellar objects, while the least intense are the elliptical and S0 galaxies. There is a spread in radiated power for most types, as shown in Figure 13.7.

The optical spectra of most radio sources are notable for their emission lines. The strength of the emission varies from barely perceptible to extremely strong, many times the strength of the continuum. The most commonly observed emission lines are those of [O II] $\lambda3727$, [Ne III] $\lambda3869$, Hβ $\lambda4861$, [O III] $\lambda4959$, and [O III] $\lambda5007$. Absorption lines, if present, are very inconspicuous for galaxies with strong emission lines. The emission lines of the quasi-stellar sources are often very broad.

Optical and Radio Energies. The total amount of energy radiated by a normal luminous galaxy is about 10^{43} ergs/sec. Cygnus A, a particularly luminous galaxy and a radio source, has a total optical luminosity of 4×10^{44} ergs/sec, of which about half is contributed by emission lines. The radio emission from Cygnus A, for comparison, is 3×10^{44} ergs/sec. The range of emitted energies at radio wavelengths is from 10^{40} to 10^{45} ergs/sec for various objects.

The physical process that caused or is causing the emission of radio energy must be a very energetic one. From the optical emission lines in some radio sources, it has been calculated that the total kinetic energy involved in mass motions in the sources is on the order of 10^{55} erg. On the assumption that the radio energy emitted is synchrotron emission, it has been calculated that the total energy in the high-energy particles must be on the order of 10^{56} to 10^{60} erg. This figure includes the energy in the magnetic field necessary to maintain the synchrotron process.

Mechanisms. The radio galaxies can only be explained as the result of some gigantic explosion or outburst, probably in the nucleus of the galaxy. It is clear from the high rate of radiation that the time scale of the outburst is short, on the order of 10^3 to 10^7 years, and thus these events may recur in galaxies. Perhaps all large galaxies have been strong radio sources several times already in their lifetimes.

The mechanism of the violent event is not understood, though

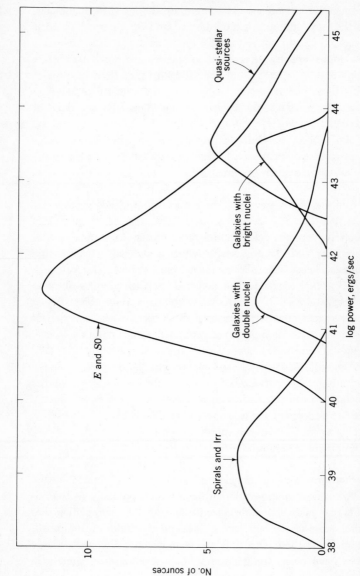

FIGURE 13.7   Distribution of radio sources according to radiated power and optical type.

1. *Collisions*. The first explanation of radio galaxies was that they are two galaxies in collision, the radiated energy being generated by the collision of gas clouds of each. This idea is no longer believed able to explain most radio galaxies, which are single galaxies.

2. *Antimatter*. Another hypothesis is that the radio galaxies are the result of interactions of normal stars with antimatter, and the interacting particles are annihilated. This is improbable, as antimatter is not generally believed to exist freely in space.

3. *Accretion*. If a galaxy accretes matter from outside it and the matter falls into the center of the galaxy, an explosion caused by the collapse of this matter might cause plasma jets to stream out. This idea does not seem to work in general for galaxies, but might apply to certain ellipticals.

4. *Formation*. It has been proposed that galaxies that are in the process of formation from intergalactic material might release large amounts of radiation. This, however, cannot apply to the majority of radio galaxies, which *seem* to be old, well-established star systems.

5. *Magnetic Flares*. A suggested explanation of how magnetic energy might be released is that spiral arms might wind up so tightly that discharges occur in the center. This requires large angular momentum and considerable gas, neither of which is present in *all* radio galaxies.

6. *Supernovae*. If stars are very densely packed in the nucleus of a galaxy, then a supernova explosion there might set off a chain reaction of supernovae. It has not been proven, however, that such a sequence could actually occur. A second hypothesis involving supernovae is that they occur in the nucleus at a high frequency because of a high rate of stellar evolution there. If a very dense nucleus is made up of very luminous stars, continuously being formed, then they will rapidly evolve to the supernova stage and maintain a long-term source of high energy.

7. *Gravitational Collapse*. An idea related to the supernova-rich nucleus is the hypothesis that stars of high mass, such as 10^6 solar mass, form in the galaxy's nucleus and then evolve rapidly until their nuclei collapse. The gravitational energy released in such a collapse can be very considerable.

There will no doubt be other explanations of the radio galaxies proposed after this chapter is written, and one of these may turn out to be more attractive than the explanations above. At this time, however, the problem is not solved.

*14 *   cosmology

Cosmology is the study of the nature of the universe as a whole, of its structure and its history. The cosmological problem remains largely unsolved, and it is only possible to discuss various hypothetical models (usually mathematical) of the universe and to point out the types of observations that hopefully will lead some day to a definite choice.

There are several good books at a readable level dealing in detail with cosmology; some of these are listed in the bibliography of this volume. The treatment of the subject here will be brief and selective.

APPROACH

The cosmological problem is an extremely complicated one. Vast simplifications are necessary to treat all that we know of the universe in terms of a single physical model or set of equations. Normally, a cosmologist is forced to make the following simplifying assumptions about the universe as a whole:

1. *Homogeneity*. It is usually assumed that the matter in the universe is uniformly distributed in space, on a large scale. Local irregularities, such as clusters of galaxies, galaxies, and stars, are ignored. Some cosmologies even assume an empty universe, containing no matter at all.

2. *Isotropy*. It is usually assumed that the velocity field of matter in the universe is isotropic. Only expansion exists, and velocities are a function only of distance, not direction. No systematic tangential velocities exist.

3. *Incoherence*. It is normally assumed that there is no effect of pressure on the model, that the universe consists of incoherent matter.

4. *Uniformity*. It is assumed that the measurable properties of extremely distant galaxies can be interpreted in familiar terms, based on knowledge of nearby galaxies. Only predictable differences, such as evolutionary ones, are allowed for.

5. *Universality*. The laws of physics as discovered and tested in the laboratory are assumed to apply, with only minor modifications perhaps, to every location in the universe. Many theories also postulate that these laws apply to the universe itself, as a whole.

In recent years attempts have been made to formulate cosmologies that do not have the limitations of all the above assumptions. For instance, cosmological models that do not assume isotropy have been worked out. These allow for rotation of the universe and shear (deviation from isotropy in direction). Even with all the simplifying postulates, however, there is already an infinite number of possible universes.

There are three general approaches from which cosmologists can choose in working on the cosmological problem. The usual approach is to assume a basic framework of physical laws, consisting of a law of gravitation and the conservation laws of mass and momentum. Normally, Einstein's theory of general relativity is the basic framework assumed, though there are some problems for which Newtonian gravitational theory is adequate and is assumed.

The second possible approach is to assume a "cosmological principle" that overrides other considerations and serves as a guide to the choice of what physical laws do or do not apply to the cosmos. The most sweeping example is the "perfect cosmological principle" of the steady-state cosmology (discussed below). This principle states that the universe always has the same, uniform, gross physical characteristics, that we do not live at some unique point in its evolution, and that the cosmic time scale has no zero point, so the universe has no evolution.

The third approach is less commonly adopted. It is based on the premise that the findings of "microphysics" (electric, magnetic, atomic, and nuclear physics) have a direct bearing on, and, in fact, result from, the nature of the universe itself. Certain dimensionless numbers, derived from known physical constants, seem strikingly arbitrary unless they have some connection with the state of the cosmos. Three cosmologies, described below, are based on attempts to explain these numbers.

GEOMETRY

A further complication of the cosmological problem is the fact that the nature of the geometry of the universe as a whole is not known. It was shown in the nineteenth century that the Euclidean "flat space" geometry is not the only self-consistent system; that, in fact, a large number of other possibilities exist. The first such geometry to be developed was that of Lobachevsky and Bolyai (independently), who replaced Euclid's axiom about parallel lines with the postulate that an infinite number of lines parallel to a given line can be drawn through a given point. This leads to the concept of "hyperbolic" space, the three-dimensional analog of a two-dimensional saddle.

Other "curved" spaces have since been developed. Einstein showed that, for a *static* (nonexpanding) universe, the principles of general relativity directly implied a positively curved universe, one that is the three-dimensional analog of the two-dimensional surface of a sphere. Such a closed universe has no boundaries, yet has a finite volume and a characteristic dimension that can be called its radius.

It can be shown that the problem of the geometry of the universe is intimately connected with the methods of measurement used to discuss spatial properties. Some scientists have argued that there is no such thing as a true or real geometry that uniquely applies to our universe, but that the geometry applicable depends entirely on the method of measurement. In the more distant realms of astronomy, the only measurements possible are those using light as a tool, so that the geometry applicable is that which the behavior of light determines. For instance, light is said to travel in a straight line in a Newtonian universe, but it can be bent by the presence of a disturbing mass in a general relativistic universe.

It is still a matter of argument whether or not geometry is truly an experimental science or whether any particular hypothesized type of space can be called "real." Modern views tend to assume that some particular geometry can be so defined as that in which physical laws and physical measurements have the *simplest* mathematical form.

In the following paragraphs a large variety of cosmologies are described, some of which do not necessarily accept Einstein's theory of general relativity. Many cosmologists, however, believe that general relativity is so well established that it may be assumed at the start. The cosmological problem then is simplified to a problem of determining what *geometry* is characteristic of the universe, as defined above.

Newton was one of the first scientists of modern times to attack the cosmological problem. He, and two centuries of scientists to follow, attempted to apply the Newtonian theory of gravitation to the universe as a whole. No satisfactory solution was found because of the following difficulties:

1. The red shift of galaxies, of course, had not been discovered, so that the concept of an expanding universe was not introduced. All early Newtonian cosmologies were restricted to static universes.

2. If the universe, as defined by the volume of space containing matter, is finite in extent, then Newtonian gravitational theory predicts that it be unstable and immediately contract to a central point.

3. If the universe instead is infinite, then Olbers showed that it cannot be homogeneous, or else the sky in all directions would be extremely bright, as bright as the average surface brightness of a star. This problem is called Olbers's paradox, and necessitates assuming (for a static Newtonian universe) either that stars are scarcer or fainter at great distances from the sun than locally or that large amounts of dust absorb distant starlight. The first alternative goes contrary to the assumption of homogeneity and to the principle that the sun should not be in a "preferred" location in the universe. The second alternative is equally unattractive, as it predicts too much dust at too high a temperature to agree with observations.

4. It was shown by Seelinger that a further difficulty of an infinite, uniform, static universe is that the inverse square law of force of Newtonian gravitation cannot apply to it, because of an illogical inconsistency that arises due to the infinite total mass of the universe.

When Newtonian cosmologies are explored for nonstable (expanding or contracting) solutions, considerably more success results.

Of course, no Newtonian model can be considered correct, as none takes into account the rather well-established tenets of special and general relativity. Nevertheless, it has been shown that Newtonian theory is a convenient and illuminating approximation to the much more complicated mathematical system of relativistic cosmologies.

GENERAL RELATIVISTIC COSMOLOGIES

The Static Einstein Model. In 1917 Einstein applied the principles of general relativity to the cosmological problem. The red shifts of galaxies had not yet been discovered, and so he considered only static models, at first. As in the Newtonian case, he found that the universe could not be infinite in extent, filling the entire Euclidean space, nor could it be a finite system surrounded by an otherwise empty, infinite, Euclidean space. Therefore, he suggested that space is not Euclidean, but is finite and positively curved.

The mathematical development of relativistic cosmologies is much too lengthy and complicated to present here, and so only some of the results of this development are given. Einstein found that the total mass of his model, M, is related to its radius, R, in a simple way:

$$G M = 1/2\pi c^2 R$$

where G is the constant of gravitation and c is the velocity of light. From this, and from the fact that the volume of spherical space is $2\pi^2 R^3$, he showed that the mean density of the universe is

$$\rho = \frac{c^2}{4\pi G R^2}$$

Thus, the radius is immediately known if the mean density can be determined. Our present best estimates of the value of ρ, determined from galaxy counts, are in the range 10^{-29} to 10^{-31} gm/cm³, leading to values for R of around 3×10^{28} cm (10^{10} pc), a not unreasonable value.

Einstein was forced to introduce a new constant, called λ, the "cosmological constant," which acted as a repulsive force at very

Kinematic Relativity. In an attempt to build a cosmological model strictly from special relativity, Milne developed a system that he called kinematic relativity. His model neglects any gravitational (or antigravitational) effects on the universe as a whole, and it considers that the universe proceeds to expand, unimpeded by any forces at all. A whole system of physics was developed by Milne from the principles of kinematic relativity, including detailed theories of dynamics and of photon and electromagnetic fields. However, there are many difficulties of the theory in detail. For instance, it does not allow for matter to be aggregated into stars and galaxies, nor does it allow other comparisons with observation to be made clearly. There are few scientists presently who believe that the kinematic relativity model is likely to be proven correct.

Modern Relativistic Models. There has been a great deal of progress in more recent years in deriving models of the universe based on general relativity. Through the efforts of Lemaitre, Robertson, Friedmann, De Sitter, Heckmann, and, of course, Einstein himself, the various possible relativistic models and the ways in which they can be distinguished observationally have been explored.

The field equations developed in connection with Einstein's theory of gravitation express a relation between the mass of the universe and its curvature, because in Einstein's view the mass causes the curvature. It is normally assumed that the universe is described by a congruent geometry with constant curvature. The metric that applies, then, has the form

$$ds^2 = c^2 dt^2 - R^2\,(t) \left[\frac{dr^2}{1 - kr^2} + r^2 \, (d\theta^2 + \sin^2\theta \, d\phi^2) \right]$$

where $r,\ \theta,$ and ϕ = dimensionless coordinates
R = a number analogous to the "radius" of space
k = curvature index of space (-1 if hyperbolic, 0 if Euclidean, $+1$ if elliptical)

Making the assumption that the universe is both homogeneous and isotropic leads to the simple result that

$$\frac{kc^2}{R^2} = \frac{8\pi G\rho}{3} - H^2$$

where ρ = present density
H = present value of the Hubble constant
G = constant of gravity
R = present value of the radius of the universe

Thus, the curvature of the universe is determined by the density (of both matter and radiation), as we found above for the simple static Einstein model. In this more general type of model, the expansion allows k to have any of the three values, since Einstein's earlier gravitational arguments no longer hold as far as k is concerned.

A great deal of effort has gone recently into much more complicated cosmologies, for which isotropy is not assumed. These have been explored by Bianci, Heckmann, Schucking, and other contemporary cosmologists, with very significant results. For instance, it has been shown that if the universe is *rotating* and expanding, then there is also *shear*, and the possibility exists that singularities in time ("the beginning") disappear and the universe oscillates between certain minimum and maximum sizes, alternately expanding and contracting forever.

STEADY-STATE COSMOLOGY

In 1948 Bondi and Gold introduced a new type of cosmology, one that adopted what they termed the *perfect cosmological principle*. This states that the large-scale aspect of the universe is independent not only of position but also of time. In this theory, the universe is infinite in extent and in age. It expands, as observed, and in order to keep the density uniform in time, it is assumed that matter is created continuously at a uniform rate just large enough to balance the loss of matter due to expansion.

Many scientists object to the concept of continuous creation of matter out of nothing, calling it an unjustified *ad hoc* assumption

However, Bondi and Gold pointed out that the attractiveness of the perfect cosmological principle might be an overriding consideration. Certainly, the steady-state model developed by them is a very simple, straightforward, and elegant one, with relatively few of the difficulties that beset evolutionary cosmological models or those easily tested by observations.

Hoyle has worked out a steady-state model based on the field equations of general relativity, modified to take into account the continuous creation of matter. His model represents a point of view different from that of Bondi and Gold in that he considers important the establishing of a definite set of equations that describes both the universe and more local phenomena. The advantage of Hoyle's approach is that it leads to many straightforward observational tests of the steady-state hypothesis.

NON-DOPPLER COSMOLOGIES

There have been several scientists who have proposed that the red shift is not a Doppler shift and that the universe is actually static. Non-Doppler cosmologies have been investigated in accordance with several rather diverse physical arguments. The theories suffer from a lack of evidence that a red shift can be produced in some other way. Most of the theorists suggest that some sort of absorption or time depletion ("tired light") occurs over large distances. One non-Doppler cosmology is that of G. Hawkins, who cites as evidence for his static-world model the fact that field galaxies (Figure 12.3) seem to fit a quadratic law of red-shift–distance.

ARGUMENTS FROM MICROPHYSICS

Dirac's Approach. The physicist Dirac pointed out in 1937 that a cosmological theory could be developed that was based entirely on considerations of the large, pure numbers of physics. These dimensionless numbers are:

1. The ratio of the electrical force to the gravitational force between proton and electron.

$$\frac{e^2}{Gm_p m_e} \approx 10^{40}$$

2. The ratio of the characteristic length of the universe (its "radius" as estimated from the value of Hubble's constant) to the classical radius of the electron,

$$\frac{c/H}{e^2/m_e c^2} \approx 10^{40}$$

3. The ratio of the mass of the universe (determined by its mean density and its "radius") and the mass of the proton,

$$\frac{\rho(c/H)^3}{m_p} \approx [10^{40}]^2$$

4. The ratio of the gravitational potential energy of the universe in the gravitational field of an object of mass m to the rest energy of that particle,

$$\frac{Gm\rho c^2 \, T^2}{mc^2} \approx 1$$

In the above equations, the following definitions apply:

G = constant of gravitation
H = Hubble's constant
e = charge on the electron
m_p = mass of the proton
m_e = mass of the electron
c = velocity of light
ρ = mean density of the universe

Dirac stated that any two of these large numbers are connected simply mathematically, as can readily be seen above, and that this is indicative that they are basically interconnected. He pointed out that some of the quantities used in the dimensionless numbers are not constant with time (for instance, ρ and H), and that it is unat·

tractive to suggest that we live by chance just when these numbers lead to values suggesting an interconnection. Thus, some of the basic physical constants must also be time-dependent. In particular, Dirac took e to be variable with time, but it can be shown that G or m_p could also have been so chosen.

Jordan's Approach. The physicist Jordan developed a cosmology from the same arguments used by Dirac, but he went into much more detail. He assumed a positive curvature to the universe (instead of flat space as derived by Dirac) and thereby was forced to abandon the principle of the conservation of mass. Also he took the constant of gravitation to be variable with time. This last hypothesis has been adopted by several other scientists and leads to interesting conclusions of both geophysical and astrophyical interest (for instance, much work of Dicke is based on this possible variation of G with time). However, Jordan's detailed exposition of the features of his cosmology has been severely criticized and is not generally accepted as a reasonable possibility.

Eddington's Approach. Sir Arthur Eddington also felt that the pure numbers of physics must in some way be connected with the nature of the universe. Instead, however, of interpreting their size as being related to the present, arbitrary epoch of time, he believed that these numbers result from fundamental properties of the universe as a whole. He developed arguments by which he was able to derive, from the properties of the universe, many of the constants of atomic and nuclear physics, thereby finding an intimate connection between the two realms of nature. Many of his arguments are extremely complicated and obscure, and at present little attention is paid to Eddington's cosmological work.

COMPARISON WITH OBSERVATION

The final test of any theoretical cosmological model is comparison with the observed properties of the universe. Fortunately, we find that at the present epoch of time, tests are becoming possible with existing observational equipment. Progress in making these tests is extremely slow, as they require using the largest telescopes under the very best conditions, and both large enough telescopes and good enough conditions are extremely rare. Nevertheless, the impression at the time of this writing is that the first really conclusive tests should be made within the next decade.

There are many types of cosmological tests possible, but at this time only one of these is practical. First, some of the methods that cannot yet be used are discussed.

Mean Density. Many cosmological models directly relate the mean density, ρ, of the universe with the characteristic length (or "radius"), R, the curvature index, k, as well as Hubble's constant H, and the age of the universe, t. Thus, since H is known, an experimental determination of ρ should determine k, R, and t. The present estimate of the density of *visible* matter in the universe is $10^{-30 \pm 1}$. The large uncertainty negates any possible use of this datum cosmologically, as an immense number of models are possible within this uncertainty. Furthermore, we have no good knowledge of how much matter there is that is not visible, e.g., how much undetected matter there is between galaxies.

Galaxy Counts. For straightforward cosmological theories, such as the simpler cases of general relativity, there is a predicted rate of change of the number of galaxies counted per magnitude interval with distance. Defining q, called the deceleration parameter, as

$$q = \frac{4\pi G\rho}{3H^2}$$

a relativistic model is uniquely defined if H and q are known. For Euclidean space, $q = \frac{1}{2}$; for hyperbolic space, q is between $\frac{1}{2}$ and 0; for spherical space, q is greater than $\frac{1}{2}$; and for the steady-state model, $q = -1$. Figure 14.1 shows some of Sandage's results of computations of the relation between N, the number of galaxies per unit area of magnitude m, and m for various values of q. The present limit of photometry is still too bright for the various models to be distinguished clearly.

In this comparison, as for those discussed below, corrections to the observed magnitudes of distant galaxies must be made to account for the red shifting of the spectrum, as well as aperture and evolutionary effects. The latter are no doubt very large for the most distant galaxies, which, for an evolutionary expanding universe, appear much younger to us than do nearby galaxies. These corrections are not always easy to evaluate.

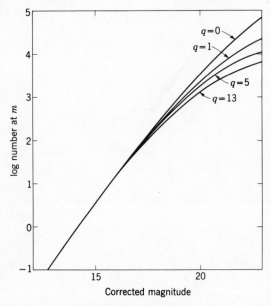

FIGURE 14.1   Curves for the number of galaxies of various magnitudes, plotted for different values of q. (After Sandage.)

Counts of extragalactic radio sources (unidentified sources in the general field) as a function of radio brightness are also of interest in this connection. If the assumption is made that all radio sources have about the same absolute flux density, S_0, then the number seen should be proportional to $S^{-3/2}$, except for cosmological effects. For all theoretical cosmologies, the predicted values for the exponent of S are greater than $-3/2$, but presently observations are giving values less than $-3/2$ (about -1.7). This suggests that the density of sources increases with distance, probably because of evolutionary effects. Radio sources may have been much more common in the early history of the universe. It is also possible, of course, that they are just not homogeneously distributed in space.

Galaxy Diameters. The apparent sizes of distant galaxies also vary with distance in a way different for different models. Sandage has computed curves for various values of q (Figure 14.2), which

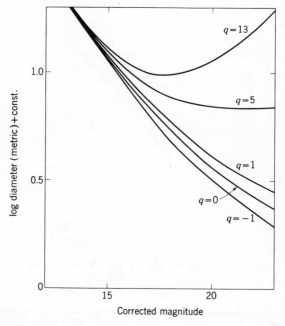

FIGURE 14.2 The relationship between diameters and magnitudes of galaxies. (After Sandage.)

show that for metric diameters there is a minimum size reached beyond which the diameters increase again with distance. For isophotal diameters (referred to a particular surface brightness) there is no such minimum, however.

Age of the Universe. All evolutionary cosmologies give a relation between their properties and the true age of the universe. Thus, if we can independently find this age, certain restrictions on possible cosmological models are established. For models with no cosmological constant ($\Lambda = 0$) and no pressure, the age is a function only of H and q (present values). For instance, for the simple case of $k = 0$, and $q = \frac{1}{2}$ (Euclidean space),

$$Ht = 2/3$$

where t is the age of the universe. From present data, H^{-1} is about 10^{10} years, and the oldest stars are about that age, also (perhaps 2×10^{10} years), but the uncertainties are too large for these data to be decisive in selecting a value of q.

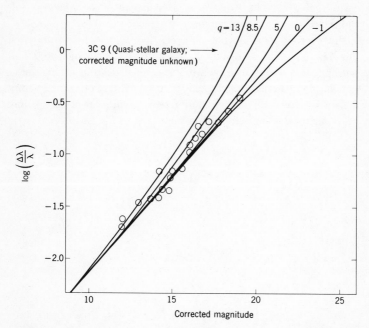

FIGURE 14.3   Curves for various models of the universe showing red shift ($\Delta\lambda/\lambda$) plotted against corrected magnitude. Some measured points are indicated. (After Sandage).

Deceleration. The most successful test of world models is the deceleration test, which examines the relation between the red shift of a galaxy and its (corrected) magnitude. Because of the large light travel time for distant galaxies, we are able to sample the rate of expansion of the universe as a function of time in the past by looking farther and farther out into space. Different values of q give different relations between these two observables, and the differences are measurably large for objects near present observational limits.

Figure 14.3 shows curves plotted by Sandage for various models, as well as positions of some distant objects. The most distant are the quasi-stellar radio sources, the absolute magnitudes of which are not well enough known for us to enter values for their corrected apparent magnitudes. When these luminosities are established, it is clear from Figure 14.3 that a value of q will be well determined, and the cosmological problem may be solved.

However, it must be remembered that a solution results from this determination of q only if the universe is homogeneous and isotropic, if it is described by a Riemannian space of constant curvature and by general relativity, and if $\Lambda = 0$. If any of these assumptions is incorrect, then much more research will be necessary before the nature of the universe is understood.

PROBLEMS, REVIEW AND
DISCUSSION QUESTIONS

Chapter 1

1   What are the most urgent problems of extragalactic research today?
2   Summarize the various observable properties of galaxies. What important properties cannot be observed?

Chapter 2

1   What is the value of classification of galaxies?
2   What is the minimum axial ratio achieved by elliptical galaxies?
3   To what extent does the spectrographic classification system of galaxies omit important information, and to what extent does it include important information not in other systems?

Chapter 3

1   If a photoelectric photometer is used to measure the integrated luminosity of a distant galaxy, what five corrections should be made before this luminosity represents all the light emitted by the stars in the galaxy?
2   The galaxy NGC 127 has the colors $B - V = 1.03$, $U - B = 0.46$. Its integrated absolute magnitude is -18.50. How would its colors and magnitude change if 10^9 cool dwarf stars, with $M_V = +10.00$, $B - V = +1.60$, $U - B = +1.50$, were added?

Chapter 4

1   Why cannot the concepts of population I and II be applied to other galaxies?
2   What are possible explanations of the presence of excited gas in elliptical galaxies?
3   If a galaxy contains 0.05 percent of its mass in the form of dust, make an estimate of the amount of the effect on its total luminosity.

1   What conceivable models of the mass distribution in a galaxy are not mentioned in this chapter?
2   What are possible arguments against the nuclear-velocity dispersion method of mass measurement?

Chapter 6

1   What possible reasons might explain the presence of "blue globular clusters" in the LMC and SMC, but not in our Galaxy?
2   What are the best methods for measuring the distances to the Magellanic Clouds?

Chapter 7

1   Why might there actually be more than 17 galaxies in the local group (two reasons)?
2   Which of the local-group galaxies have been most thoroughly studied and why?

Chapter 8

1   What two explanations possibly account for color differences across spiral arms?
2   Apply these ideas quantitatively to Figure 8.3.

Chapter 9

1   What can be said about the orbits of the Sculptor and Fornax galaxies?
2   To what distances can presently available survey telescopes detect Sculptor-type galaxies?

Chapter 10

1   How many dwarf galaxies like Sculptor would be needed in the Coma cluster to explain the 10^2 error in its total mass implied by the virial theorem results? Is this answer reasonable? Explain.
2   Argue observationally and theoretically for and against the idea that the luminosity function of galaxies has no maximum point.

Chapter 11

1   Outline the possible history of M 31 and of M 32.

1 Evaluate, considering observational problems as well as intrinsic uncertainties, the various methods of distance determinations of galaxies.

Chapter 13

1 What reasons can you give for expecting at least weak continuous radio emission from all types of galaxies?

2 Give arguments for and against the idea that all radio galaxies have the same explanation, differing only in the time since the causal event.

Chapter 14

1 Discuss arguments for and against adopting the many simplifying assumptions of theoretical cosmologies.

2 What are possible methods of testing the "microphysical" cosmologies? Which, if any, of these cosmologies are consistent with other models described in this chapter?

3 Why are the distant quasi-stellar galaxies and radio sources so important to cosmology?

BIBLIOGRAPHY

The following books are recommended for further reading:

Baade, W.: "Evolution of Stars and Galaxies," Harvard University Press, Cambridge, Mass., 1963.

Bondi, H.: "Cosmology," Cambridge University Press, London, 1961.

De Vaucouleurs, G., and A. De Vaucouleurs: "Reference Catalogue of Bright Galaxies," University of Texas Press, Austin, Tex., 1964.

Hubble, E. P.: "Realm of the Nebulae," Dover Publications, Inc., New York, 1958.

McVittie, G. C. (ed.): "Problems of Extragalactic Research," The Macmillan Company, New York, 1962.

Page, T. (ed.): "Stars and Galaxies," Prentice-Hall, Inc., Englewood Cliffs, N.J., 1962.

Sandage, A. R.: "The Hubble Atlas of Galaxies," Carnegie Institution of Washington, Washington, D.C., 1961.

Shapley, H.: "Galaxies," Harvard University Press, Cambridge, Mass., 1960.

Shapley, H.: "The Inner Metagalaxy," Yale University Press, New Haven, Conn., 1957.

Whitrow, G. J.: "The Structure of the Universe," Hutchinson & Co., (Publishers), Ltd., London, 1949.